ORMSKIRK BOARD OF HEALTH REPORT, 1850

By Robert Rawlinson

With an introduction by Audrey Coney, 1991

Reprinted by Lancashire County Books
1991

The Ormskirk Board of Health Report

Report first published by the General Board of Health, 1850

This facsimile reprint edition published by Lancashire County Books, 143 Corporation Street, Preston, Lancashire, 1991.

This edition, © Copyright, Lancashire County Books, 1991
Introduction, © Audrey Coney, 1991

Introduction typeset by Carnegie Publishing Ltd, Maynard Street, Preston
Printed by T. Snape & Co. Ltd., Boltons Court, Preston.

ISBN 1 871236 04 5

Contents

Introduction

by Audrey Coney

THE sanitary state of early-Victorian Ormskirk was incredibly bad, and Robert Rawlinson records in graphic detail the dire condition of this Lancashire town in 1849. Documentary evidence such as this is a valuable aid to understanding the environment within our towns and cities in the pre-public health era. As far as Ormskirk is concerned, no other document sheds as much light on the condition of the town at this time. Rawlinson sent reports to the General Board of Health in London for several places in Lancashire and elsewhere. His report on Ormskirk is the first of a series to be re-published by Lancashire County Books. Though his work is usually available for consultation in certain libraries and record offices, reproduction of his Lancashire material will make these documents available to a wider readership.

Robert Rawlinson had a personal involvement with Lancashire. He was the son of a Chorley builder, Thomas Rawlinson, and Grace Ellice of Exeter. Robert was actually born in Bristol in 1810, but his parents moved north soon after his birth, and he was educated in Lancaster. As a youth he assisted his father in his building, contracting and millwright business. In 1831 Rawlinson began to work for Jesse Hartley, the famous dock engineer, and was employed on the Liverpool docks project. In 1836 he started employment as railway engineer for Robert Stephenson, and assisted in the construction of the London and Birmingham Railway. Robert Rawlinson returned to Liverpool in 1840 as assistant surveyor to the Corporation, a position he held until the end of 1844. Then, on Jesse Hartley's recommendation, he was appointed engineer to the Bridgewater Canal Trust. By 1847 Rawlinson was again engaged on work in Liverpool. When the architect of St. George's Hall, Harvey Lonsdale Elmes, retired through ill-health Rawlinson was involved with the building's completion. As consultant engineer he designed the vaulted ceiling over the great hall and, by introducing hollow blocks into its construction, reduced the weight from a possible one thousand tons to six hundred tons.

Liverpool was at this time undergoing its own public health crisis, and a supply of fresh and uncontaminated water was of paramount importance. Rawlinson submitted a scheme for supplying the town from Bala Lake in North Wales. His ideas were rejected in favour of Rivington in Lancashire, which was thought to be a cheaper alternative. Years later, when Welsh water did eventually flow through Liverpool's taps, its source was a district not far removed from Rawlinson's original suggestion. It was perhaps while in Liverpool that Rawlinson made his initial acquaintance with public health affairs. In the 'unhealthiest town in England' he surely saw at first hand the human misery that evolved from poverty, overcrowding and lack of sanitation. When the Public Health Act was passed in 1848, he was appointed inspector to the General Board of Health. In his new capacity Rawlinson conducted the board's first inquiry and wrote its first report (on Dover).

Cushioned as we are today by decades of sanitary improvement, it is easy to forget that few of our early-Victorian ancestors had access to flush toilets and clean, running water. The average Englishman knew them not. Public health improvement was in its infancy in the late 1840s, and initial reform measures tended to be directed towards urban areas. It was here that they were needed the most. At the beginning of the nineteenth century only about twenty per cent of the population of England and Wales lived in towns of over five thousand inhabitants. By 1851, as industry expanded, that figure had risen to 54 per cent. Now, for the first time ever, more people lived in towns than in the country. Rapid urban development, on a scale never previously experienced, created atrocious sanitary conditions. Houses, wells and privies were often shared by several families, and dwellings frequently lay in close proximity to shippons, pigsties and slaughterhouses. With no efficient system of rubbish removal, mounds of refuse and raw sewage formed vast reservoirs of infection. Inevitably this contaminated a water supply which was rarely, if ever, adequate. The situation in more rural areas was far from perfect but there, where the population was more dispersed, the countryman's well and the farmyard midden were health hazards to a lesser degree.

The inevitable result of the urban population explosion was a rise in rates of disease and death. The town was soon regarded as a dangerous place in which to live, and the chances of an early demise increased for the inhabitants of the poorest and most over-populated districts. Poor hygiene, malnutrition, long working hours in an unhealthy atmosphere, and damp, dirty and overcrowded homes provided scant resistance to infection. At greatest risk were those who were poor in health and pocket, very young, or getting on in years. The connection between environment and epidemic disease was rammed home by Edwin Chadwick's survey of the sanitary condition of England in 1842. Chadwick contrasted death rates in town and country, and between working, middle and upper classes. His figures showed that, in some places, the life expectancy for labourers and their families was almost half that of the upper classes. The nation's health required urgent improvement, and remedial measures were particularly needed in the region of sanitary reform.

In 1846 the first of a series of Nuisances Removal Acts allowed local justices to prosecute those responsible for mounds of filth, dirty homes and overflowing drains and cesspools, and established the Poor Law authorities for rural areas. More far reaching was the Public Health Act of 1848, which set up a General Board of Health and empowered local authorities to establish local boards. A Board of Health had been set up before, but this was the result of the cholera epidemic of 1832. The local boards which sprang up across the country at this time were transient affairs. Those established under the 1848 Act were the first with any degree of permanence. Local authorities now had power to manage the refuse and sewerage system and the water supply. They could regulate offensive trades, such as slaughtering, remove 'nuisances' and deal with cellar dwellings and houses unfit for human habitation. They could provide burial grounds, parks and public baths, and their powers were backed with rights to levy a local rate and to buy land. However, a local board was not an obligatory body: a preliminary inquiry by the General Board's inspector was required before the Act could be adopted for any particular place. This inquiry was held if at least ten per cent of those rated for poor relief petitioned for it. Only if the overall death rate in a district exceeded 23 per thousand could the General Board of Health intervene and force authorities to set up a local board. Though limited in scope, the 1848 Act was an indication that the state now acknowledged some responsibility for the nation's health. The early Victorians did not fully understand why an insanitary environment and a high death rate were connected, but they certainly recognised the link between dirt and epidemic disease. This legislation was a major effort to combat both.

In the heartland of the industrial revolution, Lancashire had more than its share of muck and sickness. However, Ormskirk was not, at face value, a likely candidate for a public health crisis. This was no highly industrialised area, but the trading centre for the agricultural south-west Lancashire coastal plain. In the 1840s Ormskirk was a market town of less than six thousand inhabitants, and surrounded by fertile countryside with arable fields and green pastures. Though no longer home to Lancashire Quarter Sessions, the Earl of Derby's court leet continued to meet annually. The Earl re-built the town hall in 1779, and the four main streets contained several elegant Georgian houses and gardens. The homes of the town's professional class lay beside the inns, houses, and shops of tradesmen and craftsmen. On long and narrow plots of land at right-angles to the streets, the houses of Ormskirk suggest ancient burgage property. Indeed, the nineteenth-century town overlaid a medieval framework, for its market and borough charters date from the end of the thirteenth century. Several centuries of commercial enterprise shaped its Victorian face. The town centre was first mapped in 1609, and this seventeenth-century street pattern was essentially the same two and a half centuries later, when the first ordnance survey maps were published.

However, the first half of the nineteenth century saw a dramatic rise in population, which increased from 2,554 in 1801 to 4,891 in 1841. It reached 5,141 in 1847 and may have topped 5,760 by 1849. To accommodate these extra inhabitants, several hundred new houses were constructed. The overall effect was not so much to expand the urban area outwards, as to increase the concentration of dwellings within the town. The map in Rawlinson's report gives some idea of the congestion of Ormskirk, but it is only by inspecting a really large-scale plan of the town, such as the five feet to one mile plan, dated 1851 but actually surveyed in 1849, that its magnitude can be appreciated. Cottages were crammed into any available space, which often meant the back premises of extant buildings. These yards already contained many ancillary constructions: a motley array of older dwellings, sheds, stables, breweries and slaughterhouses. As the demand for housing increased, it is likely that many places formerly used as animal shelter or workplace were used to live in. The yards and alleyways were largely undrained, and some had neither privy nor water supply. They were totally unsuitable for human habitation.

As the population rose, so did the death rate. Between 1819 and 1823 it was about 17.6 per thousand inhabitants. It climbed to 23.1 per thousand between 1829 and 1833, and was 25.2 per thousand in the years from 1839 to 1843. Between September 1847 and September 1849 it leapt appallingly, and was believed to be a staggering 46.1 per thousand. Not even the most unhealthy district of London in 1849 could match a figure like this. In these years Ormskirk suffered repeated attacks of 'fever' which became endemic in the areas of worst squalor. Cholera, most feared of all diseases, arrived in 1849. Ormskirk medics were in no doubt as to where the problem lay. The sick and dying came in greatest numbers from the overcrowded, undrained yards and alleys. Many were Irish, who had fled from a country in the grip of famine.

These recent immigrants were neither the first nor the only Irishmen in Ormskirk, for in 1841 about four hundred inhabitants (around one-twelfth of the population) were born in Ireland. For some time seasonal harvesters had crossed the sea to England to work on Lancashire farms. The Liverpool to Ormskirk railway, which opened in 1849, was built with Irish labour. Inevitably some immigrants found more permanent occupations, and the vast majority of Ormskirk's lodging-houses were run by Irishmen. In 1849 there were sixty such places in the town. Usually located in insanitary courtyards, they provided cheap accommodation in appalling conditions. But Irish hospitality is legendary. When the potatoes withered and blackened in their home country, and as starving compatriots arrived sick and weary in a foreign land, it is likely that Ormskirk's lodging-houses turned few, if any, away.

The influx began in 1847 when tens of thousands of men, women and children reached Liverpool by boat from Dublin. While some travelled onwards to America, many stayed in the port or settled in urban areas like Manchester. An unknown number reached Ormskirk. The Ormskirk Irish frequently came from County Mayo, one of the remotest areas of Ireland, and perhaps many were returning to a place already familiar from harvesting days. They left behind a country which was poor and backward, where home was often a windowless one-room cabin, with a pig and a midden beside the door. Now in a foreign land, it is only natural that they sought shelter where cultural ties were strong. With the means to pay for only the most meagre accommodation, these newest immigrants were forced into the cheapest lodging. Ormskirk was to prove a deadly refuge.

Picture if you can the scenes when the town's lodging-houses were inspected in 1849. Two examples, one from the Hants Lane area and one from Aughton Street, will suffice. The Hants Lane district was regarded as among the worst in Ormskirk. The main approach to

Howard's Yard was from Southport Road. There may have been other houses in this yard, but only one was a lodging-house. The Irish occupant, his wife and two children lived in a building with two rooms, average size twelve feet by fourteen feet. The single bedstead and three mattresses on the floor provided ample sleeping accommodation for a family of four. It was woefully inadequate for the thirteen lodgers also in residence. Indeed, this wretched hovel could contain as many as twenty. Neither inside nor out was there a vestige of a water supply: no pump, not even a well. Sewage from privy and midden flowed across the yard surface and out into Green Lane. It is little wonder that it was recorded as filthy and 'past description'.

This building did at least have a window. In Fairbridge Yard, off Aughton Street, only a hole in the roof ventilated one of the seven lodging-houses there. Its two rooms averaged fourteen feet by fifteen feet, with a total of three bedsteads and two mattresses on the floor. Seventeen people were in that building on the day that it was inspected: twelve lodgers and the resident family of five. In fact the place was considerably less than half full. On occasions, an unbelievable forty lodgers had crammed within its grimy walls. There was a pump for water in the yard outside, and two earth closets, but the overflow from the latter and from a nearby pigsty drained across the yard and out into the street. The place was described as very dirty, with a quantity of unwholesome matter in front of the door.

Pigsties, middens and unwashed bedding were no cause for surprise to the Irish, but they now encountered them amidst high-density housing. As the first starving immigrants converged on the town in that fatal spring of 1847, many were already ill. The squalor in certain areas of Ormskirk was a fertile breeding ground for diseases with high mortality rates. Disaster was inevitable, and with the Irish it arrived.

On 8 April the Board of Guardians used powers provided by the Nuisances Act to initiate proceedings against the occupiers of two particularly dirty houses. They also recognised the need for a fever shed. It was not long before sickness was widespread. In June the medical officer succumbed to fever, and his successor resigned after only one week. As the workhouse filled with the sick poor, Ormskirk inhabitants were ordered to clean out their middensteads, clear their drains, and whitewash their homes. In October, Surgeon Symonds dealt with 563 cases of sickness of which 'fever' accounted for 455. It is not clear what types of illness were treated over this six-month period, but it seems likely that typhus, or intestinal infections such as typhoid and dysentery, were largely to blame.

Disease was not always diagnosed accurately by early-Victorian doctors, and it was not until 1869 that typhoid and typhus were differentiated. Both illnesses produced a rash, but only typhoid produced diarrhoea. The typhoid bacterium was ingested through infected food and water, while typhus – a rickettsial disease – was spread mainly by the faeces of the body louse. Typhus spread rapidly in cheap lodging-houses, where dirty bedding was used by a succession of occupants. It was often known as gaol fever or Irish fever. There were, of course, other causes of illness, and before Ormskirk's crisis was over respiratory infections were to take a terrible toll. As the death rate climbed it outstripped the birth rate. More people died than were born in the town.

Disease was everywhere. Whilst the poorest areas bore the brunt of its onslaught, there were many wealthier townspeople who suffered infection. Given the layout of Ormskirk and its congestion, a boundary wall was inadequate protection from the bacteria which flourished in the fever-ridden yards. Here, where paving, water and toilet accommodation were minimal and at times completely absent, the midden was the chief receptacle for rubbish. These mounds of stinking refuse, depository of kitchen waste, human and animal excreta, and blood and guts from numerous slaughter houses, often rotted in the yards for at least a year. Then, fully 'fermented' they were sold off to local farmers as fertiliser. In the interim, they overflowed across undrained surfaces and out into the main street. Though the full horror of the backs of Ormskirk was concealed, the eyes and noses of more prosperous townspeople were constantly assailed.

It would be a mistake, however, to regard the remainder of Ormskirk as a clean and sparkling place. By today's standards the level of hygiene was deplorable, and the water supply came from rainwater cisterns and from pumps and wells. There was not one bath in the town; Ormskirk could boast of no more than five water closets, and three of these passed their contents into a gully in the street. Quite simply, the sewerage system of Ormskirk was hardly a system at all. Only parts of the four main streets had covered drains, and the Mere Brook, a little stream along the southerly boundary of the town, was the ultimate receptacle for quantities of raw sewage. The town's careless attitude to public health is seen in the condition of the Moor Street sewer. Severed by the cutting for the railway, its contents were left to flow down the bank to the track below.

When it came to matters of sanitation Ormskirk could collect even more black marks. Conditions within the churchyard defied description, as this place had long ago reached capacity. The weekly market and twice-yearly fairs were poorly controlled, and these events left behind yet more biological refuse. It is small wonder that, at a time when a death rate of thirty per thousand was regarded as indicative of life-threatening sanitary conditions, that of Ormskirk considerably exceeded this figure.

Robert Rawlinson came to Ormskirk in November 1849 with the town reeling from the arrival of cholera. This was truly a shock disease, which could, and did, kill within hours of the onset of symptoms. Its mortality rate was about fifty per cent. Between 1 June 1849 and 14 November 1849 the Union surgeon treated thirty cases of cholera, of which sixteen proved fatal. Contrast this death rate with the figures for diarrhoea and 'fever' during the same period; there were 117 cases of diarrhoea and eight deaths, and 101 cases of 'fever' and fourteen deaths.

Rawlinson was in Ormskirk at the request of the inhabitants who had sent a petition to the General Board of Health in London. This body may well have compelled the authorities in Ormskirk to set up a local board here anyway, for the death rate in this town was almost twice the level at which intervention was deemed necessary. Actually, it may have been slightly exaggerated, for the pre-famine population figure from the 1841 census was used to determine the death rate between September 1847 and September 1849, and by this time the number of inhabitants had increased. But it matters little which figures are used, for both indicate a bottomless pool of human misery. Of the 474 people who died in those two dreadful years, 159 of them were babies under two years old. An additional 65 older children never saw their fifteenth birthday. Shall we ever truly understand the pain they suffered, or the depth of sorrow and despair of loved ones left behind? Some things are impossible.

The appalling condition of the destitute required emergency action, and the town as a whole was in urgent need of a good supply of clean water and an efficient sewerage system. Robert Rawlinson's subsequent report recommended that a local board should be established as soon as possible, so that improvement could begin. On 13 July 1850 an Order in Council provided the authority for Ormskirk to have a local board of health. The new board was to be elected by the ratepayers, and would have the power to carry out the required remedial measures. These included the regulation of lodging-houses, supply of fresh water, installation of new drains and sewers, and street and courtyard cleansing.

Amazingly, the proposed reforms were not greeted with relief in all quarters of the town. The prospect of paying rates for supplying water and for removing sewage from the most dilapidated hovels was greeted with less than delight by some landlords. Rawlinson, who combined his role of inspector to the General Board of Health with his earlier profession of engineer, was accused of creating work for himself. Those who cried out loudest against high rates were often those whose buildings were in the worst condition. By implying, wrongly, that impoverished occupiers would contribute to the cost of improvement, this anti-public-health faction gained a certain amount of support from the poorer sectors.

Loud in condemnation of the 1848 Public Health Act and Ormskirk's local board was Joseph Stoner, a grocer in the town. This is surprising because Stoner was vice-chairman of the board of guardians, and in 1849 had accompanied Rawlinson on his tour of inspection of the town. At the inquiry he expressed concern that the crisis had increased the amount expended in poor relief, and believed that a board of health would be beneficial provided that it was economical. However, Stoner was far from popular amongst the worthies of Ormskirk, and his name is not among the members of the new governing body who drew up health bye-laws for the town in 1851. However, it *does* appear among those who stood for election to the local board in 1852. This authority was now accused of wasting public money, and the election was accompanied by mounting acrimony on both sides.

Stoner failed in his election bid. He was subsequently involved in organising a petition to parliament, which was circulated around the town, and which referred to irregularities in the way the local board was elected. For his 'unjustifiable charges' against Ormskirk solicitor William Welsby, clerk to the local board of health, Stoner was apparently forced into a public apology. Despite such bitter contention, the election of 1852 was accompanied by a degree of levity, mainly at Stoner's expense. Of foreign extraction and a comparative newcomer to the town, the grocer was portrayed as a Russian bear who hated pure water and who became almost ungovernable at the prospect of it. The man had many confrontations with those in the forefront of Ormskirk's public life, and his propensity for upset lives on in an undated poem, *A few incidents in the life of Stunner Joe!*: '. . . Can you find a year, since I came here, In which there's been no row!'. Grassroots politics were born of stuff like this.

In 1850 the Order in Council which authorised a local board of health for Ormskirk was one of the first for Lancashire. This new governing body was established amidst a stormy political climate, and a welter of small-town squabbles surrounded the start of a long and arduous road to health. Ormskirk's local board was a direct response to an appalling death rate, the shock appearance of cholera and a terrible emergency. Panic rather than pioneering spirit lay behind its initiation.

Audrey Coney
June 1991

Further Reading

Audrey P. Coney, 'Mid-nineteenth century Ormskirk: disease, over-crowding and the Irish in a Lancashire market town', in *Transactions of the Historic Society of Lancashire and Cheshire*, vol. cxxxix (1990), pp 83–111.

Dictionary of National Biography, Supplement. Article on Sir Robert Rawlinson. (Oxford U.P., 1901.)

Lynn Hollen Lees, *Exiles of Erin* (Manchester U.P., 1979).

Liverpool Heritage Bureau, *Buildings of Liverpool* (Liverpool City Planning Department, 1978.)

Eric Midwinter, 'Local boards of health in Lancashire', in *Transactions of the Historic Society of Lancashire and Cheshire*, vol. cxvi (1965), pp 167–180.

Robert Rawlinson, *Public Works in Lancashire for the Relief of Distress among the unemployed factory hands, during the cotton famine 1863–66* (King, 1898.)

F. W. Stacey, *Ormskirk: the development of a 19th-century Lancashire market town* (Author, 1975).

Anthony S. Wohl, *Endangered Lives: Public Health in Victorian Britain* (Dent, 1983.)

Cecil Woodham-Smith, *The Great Hunger* (Hamilton, 1962.)

In Lancashire Record Office:

Historic Ormskirk Collection (UDOr 15)
Minutes of the Ormskirk Board of Guardians (PUS 1/2).
Map of Ormskirk 1609.
O.S. maps of Ormskirk 5ft. to one mile (1851).

PUBLIC HEALTH ACT

(11 & 12 Vict., cap. 63).

REPORT

<small>TO THE</small>

GENERAL BOARD OF HEALTH

<small>ON A</small>

PRELIMINARY INQUIRY

INTO THE SEWERAGE, DRAINAGE, AND SUPPLY OF
WATER, AND THE SANITARY CONDITION
OF THE INHABITANTS

<small>OF THE TOWN AND TOWNSHIP OF</small>

ORMSKIRK,

IN THE COUNTY OF LANCASTER.

BY ROBERT RAWLINSON, Esq.,
<small>SUPERINTENDING INSPECTOR.</small>

LONDON:
PRINTED BY W. CLOWES & SONS, STAMFORD STREET,
FOR HER MAJESTY'S STATIONERY OFFICE.
1850.

NOTIFICATION.

THE General Board of Health hereby give notice, in terms of section 9 of the Public Health Act, that on or before the 22nd of June next written statements may be forwarded to the Board with respect to any matter contained in or omitted from the accompanying Report on the Sewerage, Drainage, and Supply of Water, and the Sanitary Condition of the Inhabitants, of the Town and Township of ORMSKIRK, in the County of Lancaster; or with respect to any amendment to be proposed therein.

By order of the Board,

HENRY AUSTIN, *Secretary.*

Gwydyr House, Whitehall,
16th May, 1850.

TABLE OF CONTENTS.

PUBLIC HEALTH ACT (11 and 12 Vict., Cap. 63).

Report to the General Board of Health on a Preliminary Inquiry into the Sewerage, Drainage, and Supply of Water, and the Sanitary Condition of the Inhabitants, of the Town and Township of ORMSKIRK, *in the County of Lancaster.* By ROBERT RAWLINSON, *Esq.,* Civil Engineer, Superintending Inspector.

London, November, 1849.

MY LORDS AND GENTLEMEN,

ON Wednesday the 21st of November, 1849, according to instructions from your Honourable Board, I commenced a public inquiry at the Town Hall in Ormskirk, and received such evidence as was there brought before me by the rate-payers, and also made a personal inspection of the district, in company with the Rev. E. G. G. Hornby, William Welsby, Esq., Mr. Charles Price Symonds, Mr. Robert Morris Marsden, Mr. Thomas Kershaw, Mr. Joseph Stoner, and others. I examined the town and district, and beg respectfully to submit this Report for consideration.

According to the census of 1841, the number of inhabitants in the town and township was 4891 ;* and in November, 1848, a petition was received by the General Board, signed by 162 persons, being ratepayers, requesting that an inspector should be sent down, as hereunder stated :—

"Now, THEREFORE, we, the undersigned inhabitants of the town and township of Ormskirk, in the county of Lancaster, and rated to the relief of the poor of and within that town and township, and being one-tenth in number of the inhabitants rated to the relief of the poor of and within the said town and township, do hereby petition the General Board of Health to direct a superintending inspector to visit the said town and township ; and to make inquiry and examination with respect thereto, with a view to the application of the said Act according to the provisions of the said Act in that behalf."

[Here follow the Signatures.]

Mr. Mathew John Mason proved that on November 3rd, 1849, the proper notices were affixed within the district, on the doors of the parish church, Methodist chapel, Presbyterian chapel, Independent chapel, and Town-hall ; which notice was also advertised in the 'Liverpool Courier' of October 31st, 1849, and in the 'Liverpool Mercury' of November 2nd, 1849.

At the commencement of the inquiry there were present the Rev. E. G. G. Hornby, vicar ; the Rev. J. A. Kershaw ; Edward Boyer, Esq., Justice of Peace ; William Welsby, Esq., chairman of the Board of Guardians ; Mr. William Lax, surgeon ; Mr.

---

* Present population about 5141.

Robert Wareing, solicitor; Mr. Joseph Lyon, chairman of the Gas Company; Mr. James Palmer, solicitor; Mr. Robert Morris Marsden, surgeon; Mr. T. M. Ashton, surgeon; Mr. Charles Price Symonds, surgeon; Mr. Thomas Kershaw, chemist; Mr. Thomas Hutton, Mr. W. G. Tilsley; Mr. Joseph Stoner, Vice-Chairman of the Board of Guardians; Mr. H. Bromley, Mr. Roger Winrow, Mr. John Martin; Mr. William Higginbotham Garside, overseer; Mr. William Smith, overseer. There were also present many of the tradesmen and working men of the town, who watched the proceedings with great interest, and made many inquiries as to the probable amount of rate which would be required, the mode of choosing the local Board, and the proposed system of management.

The following Report will be found divided under the several heads, as given in the table of contents. Some of the remarks and suggestions are not absolutely necessary to the application of the Act, neither will it be imperative on the local Board to carry out all the works suggested. Surveys, plans, sections, drawings, and specifications are required, from which to furnish detailed estimates. The application of the Public Health Act will call into existence a local governing body, elected by the rate-payers, who will be provided with the power necessary to carry out proper sanitary works so much required to promote the health of the labouring man—to regulate common lodging-houses—to supply water—to construct sewers and drains—to cleanse and regulate the streets, passages, courts, and yards—to control and regulate the markets—and, if practicable, to purchase the gas-works for the benefit of the town, so as to enable one establishment, with one set of officers, to do the necessary work of the whole town, with efficiency, as with the greatest economy.

Sanitary works, properly carried out and well managed, will be an indirect and direct saving. They will reduce the poor's-rates; and waterworks, economically managed, will yield a surplus income. The same remarks apply to gasworks and markets; even sewers and drains may be made to pay their cost by a proper application of the refuse.

EARLY HISTORY OF THE TOWN.

The town and township of Ormskirk and the parish of Ormskirk are situated in the county of Lancaster, 13 miles N.N.E. of Liverpool, 13 miles W. of Wigan, 14 miles N.N.W. of Prescot, 18 miles S.S.W. of Preston, and 218 miles from London. Ormskirk is not named in the Domesday survey; but the parish, according to very credible tradition, belonged to Orm, the Saxon proprietor of Halton, who, driven from his possessions in Cheshire, established himself in Lancashire. He was probably the founder of the church; which, with his own name, now constitutes that of the parish. It is certain that a church and the name of Ormskirk, or Orm's Kirk, were co-existent in the reign of Richard I.

The church, which is dedicated to St. Peter and St. Paul, was built soon after the Conquest by Orm, the proprietor of Halton; the original edifice being much smaller than the present structure, and having a spire. On the suppression of Burscough Abbey, this church was probably enlarged, and no doubt a tower was then added to receive eight of the bells taken from the priory,* the remainder of the bells from the same abbey were removed to Croston church. The tenor bell at Ormskirk, which is said to have been the third bell in Burscough Priory, bears an extremely well executed inscription in old English characters, occupying the whole circle, round and immediately below the cannons or ears by which it is hung, with the initials "𝕽. 𝕭." and date 1497. About half-way down the bell is another inscription, and beneath this there is a neat border, beautifully cast, filled up in the centre with the rose, portcullis, and fleur-de-lis, repeated so as to occupy the whole circle of the bell.

The present body of the church was rebuilt in 1729, and the spire having been blown down in 1731, was rebuilt about 1790. The whole edifice was improved and altered in 1828; but the spire having fallen into decay, was a third time rebuilt in 1832.

By a record preserved in a manuscript collection, "Actes of Councell during the raigne of Edward 6th," it appears that the population of Ormskirk parish was 3013; and it is there stated that, upon a motion made to the lords of the council, the vicar's salary was augmented 10*l.* per annum. The population of the parish was estimated at the last census, 1841, as 13,535, exhibiting an increase since the middle of the sixteenth century of no fewer than 10,522 persons.

The dates in the parish registers of Ormskirk commence November, 1557, and the results obtained from them are :—

	1557	1558	1600	1601	1700	1701	1800	1801	1832	1833
Baptisms . . .	8	55	67	81	102	107	203	212	139	172
Marriages . . .	6	26	22	13	43	39	30	13	55	66
Burials . . .	38	143	60	75	121	153	189	221	524	239

Leland, with a want of accurate admeasurement often to be detected, in his ' Itinerary,' says :—

* There appears no foundation for the vulgar tradition that the church was built by two maiden sisters, who could not agree as to the erection of a tower or spire alone, so each built according to her wish, the one a tower, the other a spire. There is evidence in the building that the tower is an addition, and the Burscough Abbey bells indicate the cause for it.

" *Ormskirk,** a iiii. miles or v. myles from Lyrpole, and about a ii. miles from Latham ; a parock chirche in the towne, no river by yt, but mosses of eche side. *Latheham,* most part of stone, the chefest house of the Erles of *Darby,* ii. from Ormskirk, on a brook cawllid Golforden."

Camden, pursuing his route from Formby to this place, says, " From hence runs out a bold shore, with a great bend ; and further in from the sea we see Ormskirke, a market town, famous for the burial place of the Stanleys, Earls of Derby, whose chief seat Latham, a large and magnificent mansion, is in the neighbourhood."

In 14 Edward I. a royal charter, dated at Westminster, April 28, was obtained by the prior and convent of Burscough, granting to them and their successors for ever a market every week, on Thursday, at their manor of Ormeschirche, and a fair there every year for five days—on the eve, the day, and morrow of the beheading of St. John the Baptist, and the two following days, unless the market and fair be injurious to the neighbouring markets and fairs. The fairs are now held on Whit-Monday and Tuesday, and on the 10th of September; but the market continues to be held on Thursday, the day assigned in the charter of Edward I.

PARISH OF ORMSKIRK.

The parish contains six townships, of which the following forms the enumeration, with the returns of the number of inhabitants in 1801, 1811, and 1821, and the estimated annual rental of all the lands, messuages, and other buildings in each township of the parish :—

Ormskirk Par	POPULATION.					Estimated Annual Value.
	1801	1811	1821			
	Persons.	Persons.	Houses.	Families.	Persons.	
						£
Township of Bicaerstaffe	811	911	194	197	1,212	6,777
,, Burscough	1139	1492	332	332	1,755	9,142
,, Latham .	2179	2514	528	545	2,997	14,267
,, Ormskirk .	2554	3064	763	782	3,838	7,616
,, Scarisbrick	1154	1386	268	279	1,584	11,954
,, Skelmersdale	414	541	103	102	622	2,691
Total . . .	8251	9908	2188	2237	12,008	52,447

Of the 2237 families in this parish, 1112 are employed chiefly in agriculture, and 802 in trade, manufactures, or handicraft ; the remaining 323 are either engaged in professional pursuits or are unemployed.

* Ormskirk is about thirteen miles from Liverpool.

There are no extensive manufactories in the town, and the trade is circumscribed. Coals are obtained within 2 miles; and several steam-engines are in use. The town was first lighted with gas on Easter Monday, April 20, 1835.

GEOLOGY.—The town of Ormskirk stands upon the new red sandstone formation. A large tract of sandy land lies to the west and north; the millstone-grit and the coal-measures lying to the east; the Manchester and Wigan coal-field extending to within two miles of the town. Good building-stone, sand, clay, and marl are obtained in the immediate neighbourhood; and, from the character of the subsoil, all sanitary works may be accomplished at a minimum cost.

The soil of the parish is generally a dark vegetable loam, with a mixture of sand, well calculated for culture. Potatoes and carrots are grown in the district in large quantities. From this cause there is more land in tillage in the parish of Ormskirk than is usual in the Lancashire parishes, and the arable and pasture lands may here be safely estimated as in very nearly equal proportions. Rents are from 40*s.* to 100*s.* the statute acre.

Peat-mosses abound in the parish of Ormskirk, which contains Bickerstaffe Moss, Hosker Moss, Scarsbrick Moss, and Burscough Moss, from each of which are frequently dug up trees, principally oak and fir, which have been buried for ages.

The remains of peat, with timber, are washed out of the beach on the Lancashire and Cheshire shores; they have been dredged up in the Victoria Channel; and, some years ago, stumps of trees might be seen at Leasowe, the roots having firm hold of the earth, showing that those trees, whose remains these were, grew upon that spot. Many prostrate trunks have been laid bare, as also bones and horns of deer. In sinking a well at the same place, besides this surface-moss, two other formations of a similar character were passed through within a depth of 30 feet, red and blue clay intervening betwixt each layer of sand and moss.* These facts, with the imbedded trees of oak, fir, and animal remains, of the upper formation, being found several feet below the present tidal flow, indicate considerable change in the relative level of land and water, and the geologist may reasonably infer that any motion the earth's crust may have in this island at present is downwards. The geological evidence of the whole coast of England more or less supports the hypothesis.

METEOROLOGY.—The prevailing winds are from the west, south, and intermediate points. The rainfall varies from 29 inches to 40 inches per annum. The climate is influenced by the proximity of the sea, and is favourable to health. Proper sanitary works and regulations are alone required to render Ormskirk and the neighbourhood extremely healthy.

---

* In each layer of embedded moss remains similar to those in the upper moss are found,—that is, timber and bones, not however perfectly identical.

FALL of RAIN at LIVERPOOL and MANCHESTER.

	At Liverpool. Inches.	At Manchester. Inches.
Year ending Aug. 30, 1847 .	. 37·03	33·075
Ditto ditto, 1848 .	. 49·74	49·79
September, 1848 .	. 3·36 . . .	3·43
October . .	. 4·34 . .	5·58
November . .	. 2·40 . .	2·61
December . .	. 2·25 . .	3·40
January, 1849 .	. 3·20 . .	4·67
February . .	. 1·54 . .	1·95
March . . .	. 0·77 . .	0·58
April . . .	. 2·39 . .	1·25
May . . .	. 3·002 . .	3·15
June . . .	. 1·52 . .	1·64
July . . .	. 6·03 . .	4·88
August . .	. 4·19 . .	2·62
	34·992	35·76

(left margin: Year ending Aug. 1849.)

REMARKS.—In making any calculations from the rainfall of a district for purposes of a water-supply to be collected from gathering grounds, the least annual recorded fall must be taken. It is most fallacious to take a series of years and average their collective quantities, as few reservoirs are calculated to hold more than from three to six months' supply. In 1826 the rainfall in Manchester was about 25 inches; in Liverpool, 22¼ inches. In 1836 the rainfall in Liverpool was 22½ inches. In 1841 the recorded rainfall was 49½ inches,—more than double the volume in 1826 or 1836. In Bolton, during a period of 18 years, the highest recorded rainfall took place in 1831—62¼ inches; the lowest in 1844—34½ inches. These examples will show how much the rainfall varies at the same place.

LOCAL GOVERNMENT.—There is no local Act of Parliament in force within the district. The township is lighted with gas, under the superintendence of inspectors elected under the general Lighting Act. The streets and highways are under the control of a surveyor appointed under the general Highway Act.

AREA.—The area of the township is about 600 statute acres, chiefly land under cultivation. The greater portion of the population is concentrated at the north-west portion of the township.

RATEABLE VALUE AND NUMBER OF HOUSES.—The rateable value is 11,500*l.*; and there are about 1028 houses in the township—

Assessed at	5*l.* and under	.	.	562
Not exceeding	10*l.* ,,	.	.	237
,,	20*l.* ,,	.	.	129
,,	30*l.* ,,	.	.	48
Above . .	30*l.* ,,	.	.	52
		Total	.	1028

16 of the 52 rated above 30*l.* are publicans and brewers.

HIGHWAY RATE.

	Highway Rate.	Excused Rate.
	£. *s.* *d.*	£. *s.* *d.*
1847	262 17 6½	26 2 5¾
1848	264 7 1½	20 11 4¾

MARKETS.—The lord of the manor, through his court-leet, exercises control over the markets and fairs. These are managed by a jury of 12 men, who pay the Earl of Derby 30*l.* per annum for the tolls. Any surplus which may remain is expended on improvements in the town. This court also elects a constable and churchwarden : the former officer, however, exercises no power since the establishment of the county constabulary ; but the nomination is retained for the purpose of preserving an old custom, and to enable other parts of the machinery to be carried on. The lord of the manor, through his court-leet, formerly exercised restraint over nuisances ; but for many years there has been no effective check. At the meeting, which is only held once a-year by custom, fines have been imposed on property in a dilapidated state, but they are rarely enforced ; and the existing nuisances, as described, show what kind of check has been exercised over them of late years.

The markets are now held on the public street (Moor-street) ; the pigs and cattle create much nuisance ; and the markets generally obstruct the regular traffic through the town.

Some time ago an attempt was made to procure a local Act for the town; and, amongst other things, it was contemplated to lease the market-tolls from Lord Derby; and the late steward, Mr. Richard Earle, proposed to concede them on the rent of 30*l.* being secured to his lordship. The removal of the cattle and pig market from the street is necessary ; and it is desirable that the fairs and markets should be under the control of the local Board.

POPULATION.—The population of the township of Ormskirk, according to the last census (1841), was 4891 ; and the return of the registrar-general, for five succeeding years, shows an increase of 250, making the population, in 1847, 5141. During the last three years the number of deaths has exceeded the births by 53 ; so that a large increase of adult population must have come in from other sources. This may have arisen from the railway-works near the town, as also from a large influx of poor Irish; and it has been estimated, that, from these causes, the population may have during the last three years reached 5760.

MORTALITY.

TABLE of Births and Deaths in the Town of Ormskirk, for the last
7 years.

Year.	Births.	Deaths.	Remarks.
September 1842 . . .	164	126	Births in excess.
,, 1843 . . .	169	139	,, ,,
,, 1844 . . .	191	142	,, ,,
,, 1845 . . .	184	125	,, ,,
,, 1846 . . .	187	125	,, ,,
,, 1847 . . .	190	232	Deaths in excess.
,, 1848 . . .	203	239	,, ,,
,, 1849 . . .	257	235	Births in excess.
Total for the 7 years .	1545	1363	

DEATHS within the Township of Ormskirk, from the 26th of September,
1847, to the 26th of September, 1849, and causes, &c.

These two years give the high rate of mortality of 46.1 per thousand, or one death in 21·7 of
the entire population.

AGES.						PRIMARY CAUSES.										
Two years and under.	Two to Seven.	Seven to Fourteen.	Fourteen to Twenty-one.	Twenty-one to Thirty-one.	Above Thirty-one.	Typhus Fever.	Fever.	Cholera.	Diarrhœa.	Scarlatina.	Dysentery.	Pneumonia.	Consumption.	Inflammation of the Lungs.	Bronchitis.	Old Age.	Other causes.
159	40	25	19	55	176	37	21	18	35	29	17	32	44	22	21	23	175
474						474										

Population 5141.   The total number of deaths is 474 for two years.

DEATHS within the Township of Ormskirk from the 26th of September, 1847,
to the 26th of September, 1849, and Localities.

Aughton-street.	Worthington's-yard	Hall's-yard, &c.	Forshaw-yard.	Burscough-street.	Old-buildings.	Witters-yard.	Church-street.	Barkhouse-hill.	Green-lane.	Hants-lane.	Nixon's-yard.	Moor-street.	Chapel-lane.	Martlew's-yard.	Mill street.	Dickinson's-street	Prescott's-yard.	Scarth-hill-lane.	Fever-ward.	Union Poorhouse.	Railway.	Total.
81	3	9	10	55	12	3	37	6	19	25	4	57	37	6	8	5	10	6	47	5	2	474

NOTE.—With very few exceptions the fever ward cases arose in the township of Ormskirk.
Mr. M'Master, surgeon to the Union, died of fever caught in performing his duties.

Mr. *Stoner* stated—

" With regard to the mortality of Ormskirk and the surrounding district, I make it as here stated. Up to the year 1846, in Ormskirk, it did not exceed 24 in 1000; from which date, up to the present time, I make it 32½ in 1000 ; and I account for this great increase by the influx of Irish, in consequence of the failure of the potato crop ; and there has also been a large addition to the labouring population, in consequence of the railway works through and near the town. Liverpool, Ormskirk, Prescott, and Warrington, all suffered from the Irish immigration."

MORTALITY for the March and September Quarters of 1849.

Population.	Union.	Deaths.	Rate per 1000.
34,975	Ormskirk .	512	29¼
43,739	Prescott .	725	33½
33,038	Warrington	551	33½

From the 1st of June, 1849, to the 14th of November, the Surgeon to the Union attended and returned—

Cases of Cholera	.	.	30	Deaths from Cholera .	.	16
,, Diarrhœa	.	.	117	,, Diarrhœa	.	8
,, Fever .	.	.	101	,, Fever .	.	14
Total	.	.	248	Total Deaths	.	38

21 deaths of this number Irish.

Remarks on the excessive Mortality shown by these Tables.— The rate of mortality in Ormskirk during the years given was higher than the worst district in London during the past year of excessive disease and cholera. According to the first paragraph in Mr. Simon's Report, the rate of mortality in the city had been as under :—

" During the 52 weeks, dating from October 1st, 1848, to September 29th, 1849, there died of the population of the city of London 3799 persons.

" The rate of mortality, estimated from these *data* for a population of 125,500, would be somewhat in excess of 30 deaths out of every thousand living persons."

For the two years in Ormskirk given, out of a population of 5141, the rate of mortality was in excess of 46 deaths out of every 1000 living persons. In only one sub-district of the metropolis did the rate of mortality reach to within a small fraction of 40 deaths out of every 1000.

The cause of this fearful and startling excess in so small a population must be looked for in the tabulated returns made up by the county constabulary, and from the fact of the town having been overcrowded by fever-stricken Irish during this period, many of whom, no doubt, only came to die. But making every such allowance, the mortality has been most excessive, as, if we contrast it with the lowest suburban mortality recorded in the fifth volume of the Registrar-general's Reports for the year then under estimation, which gave a rate of 11 in 1000, the excess in Ormskirk is more than four to one.

In another part of this Report I have shown that nature has done much to make the district healthy; but the fearful state in which the poor have been allowed to live and die has produced the humiliating contrast shown. The presence of fever and cholera will not explain away this terrible excess of mortality; but it does constitute a most important additional testimony to the insalubrity of the district, made so by over-crowding, excessive filth, and a total absence of proper sanitary works and regulations. The sentences, "house very dirty," "bad smells," "no drains or water supply," "privies and middens close to the door," occur again and again in the tabulated list of public yards and lodging-houses. That which has taken place ought to be a warning, and a stimulant to improvement, or the black list of death may be repeated; for in the words of the medical officer to the city of London—

"The frightful phenomenon of a periodic pestilence belongs only to defective sanitary arrangements; and, in comparing one local death-rate with another, it is requisite to remember that, in addition to the ordinary redundance of deaths which marks an unhealthy district, there is a tendency from time to time to the recurrence of epidemic pestilence, which visits all unhealthy districts disproportionately, and renders their annual excess of mortality still more egregious and glaring."

Fever Cases.—The following statement explains in detail the number of fever cases attended by Mr. Symonds:—

CASES of Sickness and Fever attended by one of the Surgeons to the Union, District No. 1; Population 5141.

		Whole cases of Sickness.	Fever.	Remarks.
	1st Week	110	92	
	2nd ,,	131	108	Extreme sickness prevailed during this period.
October 1847	3rd ,,	119	99	
	4th ,,	107	84	
	5th ,,	96	72	
Total		563	455	

"The total number of cases of sickness and fever attended from the quarter ending September, 1847, to the same quarter ending 1849, according to the weekly returns made to the Guardians, are, cases of sickness 1285, of which 633 were cases of fever, out of which 136 deaths occurred from all causes, and about 40 deaths being from fever. This is entirely irrespective of those cases of sickness and fever attended from the dispensary.

" The great mass of fever cases are Irish, brought in from the crowded lodging-houses and other parts of the town where there are neither sewers nor drains, and where the supply of water is most imperfect. The inhabitants of these districts pay no attention to cleanliness or ventilation; the surface of the ground near and around their houses is in general unpaved. Open middens, pigsties, and cesspools are crowded upon the dwelling-houses, and, until such property is placed under some control to carry out and superintend proper sanitary works and regulations, I consider that cases of sickness and fever must more or less be common. Most of the cases in the lists given were removed to a temporary shed erected by the Guardians for fever patients, where they were kept and attended at the expense of the rate-payers; each case may have remained on an average three weeks, and some cases have remained upwards of six months. The cost per week has averaged about 5s. each case. During this summer I have attended about 36 cases of cholera, out of which there were 19 deaths; most of these cases have occurred where fever is common.

(Signed) " CHARLES PRICE SYMONDS,
" Surgeon."

Table of Poor's-rates and Out-door Relief.

AN Account of Poor's-rates for the Township of Ormskirk, for two years, ending the 25th of March, 1849.

	£.	s.	d.
Amount of Rates from 25th March, 1847, to 25th March, 1849	3178	4	8½
Amount collected from 25th of March, 1847, to 25th of March, 1849	2392	2	2½
Excused	117	9	0
Irrecoverable	82	8	10

Supplied by the Assistant-Overseer.

The sums expended in Out-door Relief have been for the respective years as shown in the following Table :—

		£.	s.	d.
Out-door Relief for	1845	569	18	0
,, ,,	1846	498	13	0
,, ,,	1847	578	0	0
,, ,,	1848	1095	8	0
,, ,,	1849	599	12	0
Total for 5 years	. .	3341	11	0

According to the evidence of the relieving officers, the largest amount of out-relief is expended in the most filthy district. Where there is neglected filth there is disease, and in such places the money of the rate-payers is expended. The owners of such property receive rent from tenants who not only are excused all payment of rates, but they are the very parties who expend them.

Surely it will be a wise and equitable provision to make the owners of such property responsible for its proper improvement.

Extract from Report of the Ormskirk Dispensary.—The following extract from the annual Report of the Ormskirk Dispensary will also assist to show, in conjunction with the returns of the medical officers of the union, the excessive amount of sickness in the township:—

"The expenditure for the Ormskirk Dispensary during the last year has been unusually large; this has been occasioned by the extent to which out-patients have been visited by the medical officers, by the necessary repairs of the building, and by making such alterations in the interior arrangement as the committee hope will render it much more convenient and commodious.

"Though the balance-sheet shows a considerable deficiency, yet it is very gratifying to find that, notwithstanding the pressure of the times, particularly in agricultural districts, the subscriptions have increased; while the committee have the pleasure to acknowledge the receipt of a legacy of 100*l.* (free of duty) bequeathed by the late Rev. G. Vanbrugh, formerly rector of Aughton, whose liberality and beneficence are too well known in this vicinity to need any eulogy here.

"Upon the whole, the circumstances which have occurred in regard to the Ormskirk Dispensary, during the period your committee have been in office, serve to strengthen the confidence that this most useful charity will continue to receive the same support of the public which it has so long enjoyed.

"Total number of patients admitted in the past year, 1327."
[See Table opposite.]

The following letter points out many of the evils which exist under the several heads of the inquiry, and as it is the voluntary statement of a resident medical gentleman, it ought to command the serious attention of the rate-payers of all classes; for surely the testimony of a medical man is the most disinterested possible. The selfish may think that the profession would have an interest in excessive disease, but human sympathy and large benevolence produce higher and holier motives. No persons more earnestly and actively assist and promote inquiry with a view to permanent sanitary improvement, than the gentlemen of the medical profession; and my thanks are especially due to them for their active and disinterested assistance on this as on all other occasions:—

Mr. *Marsden* states—

"I have been connected with my profession for more than twenty years, two-thirds of which period have been spent in connexion with large hospitals and dispensaries: it may therefore be supposed I have had many opportunities of forming an opinion of the causes which lead to the generation of epidemic, endemic, and contagious diseases; and the conclusion I have arrived at is, that the accumulation of animal and vegetable matter in a state of decomposition, particularly an accumulation of such matter in places destitute of drainage, is the most fertile cause of this class of diseases.

THE TREASURER in Account Current with the Dispensary, from May 1, 1848, to May 1, 1849.

DEBTOR.	£	s.	d.	£	s.	d.
To Balance in the Treasurer's hands				50	9	5¼
Cash, one year's dividend on the funded property				50	8	7
Two patients, for trusses				0	10	0
A legacy from the late Rev. G. Vanbrugh				100	0	0
Donation from a friend				1	1	0
Donation from M. F.				5	11	6
Arrears of last year				1	16	7¼
Interest on money in the Ormskirk Savings'-bank	121	18	6			
Amount of Subscriptions, as per list	5	2	0			
Deduct amount uncollected				116	16	6
Balance due to the Treasurer				40	1	1
				367	14	8¼

CREDITOR.	£	s.	d.	£	s.	d.
By Cash paid to Mr. Lax, for visits to country patients	38	18	0			
,, Mr. Ashton, for ditto	25	11	0	89	4	0
,, Mr. Symonds, for ditto	24	15	0	84	15	0
,, for Drugs						
,, Cost of 113l. 9s. 6d. Consols, 3 per cent. at 88	99	17	2			
,, Brokerage and Commission	0	6	2			
,, Various bills				100	3	4
,, Leeches, &c.				36	5	9
,, Printing, &c.				9	0	8
,, Coals				5	19	6
,, Various bills				4	9	1½
,, Insurance				15	11	3
,, One year's land-tax				1	2	6
,, Matron, one year's salary				0	3	0
,, Incidental expenses				20	0	0
				1	0	7
				367	14	8¼

" It is with this impression on my mind that I strongly urge the necessity of sewers being provided for each house, for each yard, and for each street; but as the sewers would, in my opinion, be useless unless an abundant supply of water is furnished to carry off refuse matter, I would most strongly recommend a constant supply of the best water that can be obtained for each house, yard, and street, and thus do away with the necessity of wells and pumps in the town, the water of which is in general impure, and consequently injurious to health.

" I would respectfully suggest the impropriety of burying within the walls of a church, and the propriety of closing that part of the burial-ground connected with our parish church which has been the depository of our dead for two or three hundred years, and which is so full that it cannot be disturbed to the depth of one foot without turning up the mouldering remains of some who undoubtedly expected to rest in peace, and not to have their bones exposed to the public eye year after year. I say nothing of the noxious exhalations which must arise from the constant upturning of this animal matter, poisonous in itself, injurious to health as well as to decency, and painful to witness. I may add, that I am not an advocate for intramural burials, but I do consider them less objectionable in small and comparatively open towns than in large and densely populated ones; therefore I shall leave it for your honourable Board to say whether it will be desirable to extend what we term the new burial-ground, or to form another at some easterly distance from the town.

" With regard to the slaughter-houses, I consider them the greatest nuisances in the town, and would earnestly but respectfully suggest that they be removed some distance from the town.

" One more observation and I will conclude; it is the important one of ventilation. I do consider that in many houses the windows perform the office of ventilators, but unfortunately that odious window tax closes them not only against light, but against the admission of pure air, by the admission of which we live and without which we die. Could not your honourable Board suggest the propriety of removing this tax, as opposed to sanitary improvements?

          (Signed)   " ROBERT MORRIS MARSDEN,
" To Robert Rawlinson, Esq."   " Surgeon, &c.

A local Board of Health was formed in 1848, being a committee of the Board of Guardians. Two of the county constabulary were made inspectors of nuisances, and from time to time reports have been presented to the committee forming the local Board, and under the powers of the Removal of Nuisances Act certain nuisances have been dealt with. The committee have personally inspected the town and directed such temporary cleansing as they thought fit, but for want of proper power little real good was effected, and nothing permanently.

The following tabulated returns of the county constabulary will show the actual condition of the common lodging-houses, public yards, and the state of this class of property in general.

RETURN showing the Number of LODGING-HOUSES in Ormskirk, Inmates, Rooms, &c. &c.; also the manner in which Yards, where there are Lodging-Houses, are Drained, &c.

Consecutive No.	Street.	Yard.	English, Irish, or Scotch	Married or Single.	No. of Children.	No. of Rooms.	Average Size of Rooms. (Feet)	No. of Lodgers at present.	Greatest No. at any one time	Bedsteads.	On Floor.	How Ventilated.	Privies.	Pumps.	Wells.	Amount of Rent per annum.	Mode of Drainage, if any.	REMARKS.
1	Aughton	Forshaw's	I.	M.	2	6	10×14	14	20	2	3	windows	1		1	11 4	None	Back-yard and house very dirty.
2	,,	,,	I.	W.	·	2	10×12	6	7	3	1	,,	·	·	·	5 10		House very dirty.
3	,,	,,	I.	M.	1	4	6×9	20	60	1	5	,,	·	1	·	7 10	Small sewer empties itself into the street	House very damp and dirty; inmates very dirty.
4	,,	,,	I.	M.	2	3	9×12	9	10	4	1	,,	·	·	·	6 0		Clean house; bad smell from privy, which is two yards from the door.
5	,,	,,	I.	M.	3	2	14×15	12	30	3	1	,,	1	none	none	5 4		House damp and filthy; inmates dirty; close confined yard.
6	,,	Constantine's	I.	M.	2	2	14×15	5	9	1	2	,,	·	·	·	5 4	Open drain flows into the street	House very damp and dirty.
7	,,	,,	I.	M.	4	2	14×16	9	16	2	3	skylight	·	·	·	5 4	ditto	Ditto.
8	,,	Rylance's	I.	M.	5	3	9×9	7	14	1	3	windows	·	·	·	6 10		House damp and dirty; pigsty two yards from door.
9	,,	Ball's	I.	M.	4	2	14×15	9	30	4	·	,,	1	·	·	5 4		House exceedingly dirty, and inmates also.
10	,,	,,	I.	M.	1	5	10×10	14	30	7	3	,,	·	1	none	7 7	ditto	House dirty; very bad smell.
11	,,	,,	I.	M.	4	3	10×12	6	25	2	3	,,	·	·	·	6 10		House most filthy; pigsty and middenstead adjoining house.
12	,,	,,	I.	M.	1	4	8×10	12	25	2	3	,,	·	none	·	5 4		House very dirty; bad smell.
13	,,	,,	I.	M.	1	2	12×15	7	7	·	3	,,	none	none	none	5 4	Fronts the street	Dirty house; an exceedingly bad smell.
14	,,	Fairbridge	I.	M.	4	2	8×12	4	8	1	2	,,	2	·	·	5 4	Filth from privy and pigsty flows into the street	Very dirty house; a quantity of unwholesome matter before door.
15	,,	,,	I.	M.	3	2	14×15	12	40	3	2	hole in roof.	·	1	none	4 0		Ditto.
16	,,	,,	I.	M.	2	5	7×9	12	25	6	·	window	·	·	·	6 10		House very dirty.
17	,,	,,	I.	M.	3	2	8×15	9	14	4	·	,,	·	·	·	5 0		A miserable hovel, covered with filth; two privies near door.

Table showing the Number of Lodging-Houses, &c., in Ormskirk—*continued.*

Consecutive No.	Street	Yard	English, Irish, or Scotch.	Married or Single.	No. of Children.	No. of Rooms.	Average Size of Rooms.	No. of Lodgers at present.	Greatest No. at any one time.	Bedsteads.	On Floor.	How Ventilated.	Privies.	Pumps.	Wells.	Amount of Rent per annum.	Mode of Drainage, if any.	REMARKS.
18	Aughton	Fairbridge	I.	M.	2	2	14×15	6	13	2	3	window				£7 10s.	Fronts the street	House very dirty, and inmates also.
19	,,	,,	I.	M.	2	2	14×15	7	40	6	1	,,	none	none	none	8 15	ditto	Ditto.
20	,,	,,	I.	M.		2	14×15	11	11	3	2	,,	none	none		7 10	ditto	Ditto.
21	,,	Mounsey's	I.	M.	2	2	11×11	4	6	4		,,	none	none	none	4 10	Filth from a midden flows into Aughton street	House clean; a large middenstead close to door.
22	,,	,,	I	M.	3	2	15×17	19	19	4	1	,,				5 4	ditto	House very dirty; bad smell.
23	,,	Balshaw's	I	M.	4	6	9×14	16	25	3	2	,,	1	none	1	10 0	ditto	House and inmates dirty; bad smell.
24	Church	Nixon's	I.	M.	1	3	8×9	10	15	6	1	,,	1	none	none	5 4	Small sewer from a privy empties itself in Church-street	House very dirty.
25	,,	,,	E.	M.	2	4	8×8	5	15	6		,,				5 4	ditto	House dirty.
26	Southport-road	Culshaw's	I.	M.	2	1	14×16	4	9	3	3	,,	1	none	none	3 10	All the filth from these & other premises flows on the surface into Green-lane	A wretched hovel, lost in filth; only one room for all purposes.
27	,,	Howard's	I.	M.	2	2	12×14	13	20	1		,,	1	none	none	4 0	ditto	Filthy — past description; surrounded by privies and middensteads.
28	Barkhouse-hill	...	I.	M.	3	3	11×11	5	26	4		,,	1			5 4	Fronts the lane	House dirty; midden close to back door.
29	Green-lane	...	I.	M.	2	2	13×13	14	17	2	3	,,	none	none		5 4	ditto	These are all alike lost in dirt and filth.
30	,,	...	I.	M.	2	2	13×13	12	30	4	2	,,	none			5 12	ditto	
31	,,	...	I.	M.	4	2	13×13	7	18	3	1	,,			1	5 5	ditto	
32	Hant's-lane	...	I.	M.	4	2	13×13	12	30	3	2	,,				5 4	Flows into the fiel.	House very dirty.
33	,,	...	I.	M.	2	2	10×12	9	19	2	1	,,	none	none	none	4 0	ditto	
34	,,	...	I.	S.		2	10×12	17	17	2	3	,,				4 0	ditto	Very dirty; middenstead close to the door.

No.	Township	Name	Nat.	Cond.		Room size					Rent	Drainage	Remarks
35	,,	,,	I.	M.	2 2	10×12	15 15	1 4	none none		4 0	ditto	House filthy.
63	,,	,,	I.	M.	3 3	8×8	8 8	1 2	1 none		4 0	ditto	Ditto.
37	,,	,,	I.	M.	2 1	12×15	6 20	3 1	none none		4 0	Fronts the lane	A wretched hovel; only one room for all purposes.
38	Burscough	,,	I.	W.	7 3	8×10	1 20	4 ..	1 none		7 10	Fronts the street	House clean.
39	,,	,,	E.	W.	.. 4	16×18	4 12	6 ..	1 ..		7 0	ditto	House dirty; pigsty and middenstead close to back-door.
40	Old-buildings	,,	I.	M.	3 2	13×13	15 15	5 1	.. ..		5 12	Open drain from midden, &c., flows into the main sewer in the street	Wretched beyond description; inside and outside the same filth of all kinds prevails; a sickening smell; premises very much confined by walls.
41	,,	,,	I.	M.	4 2	13×13	8 9	3 1	.. ..		5 12		
42	,,	,,	I.	W.	1 2	13×13	15 15	3 2	.. ..		5 5		
43	,,	,,	I.	M.	5 2	13×13	12 12	.. 6	.. ..		5 4		
44	,,	,,	I.	M.	4 2	10×15	6 19	4 1	1 none		4 10		House dirty; a privy and pigsty close to door.
45	Nuttall's	,,	I.	M.	1 4	11×12	6 19	5 ..	.. ..		6 4	sewer in the street	House dirty.
46	,,	,,	E.	M.	2 6	7×7	5 13	6 ..	.. 1		8 0	ditto	House clean; pigsty and privy close to the door.
47	Moor	Legs-of-Man	I.	M.	.. 2	13×15	12 17	6 1	.. ..		6 15	Drained into the main sewer	Houses exceedingly dirty; completely surrounded with pigsties, middensteads and privies of the worst description.
48	,,	,,	I.	M.	3 2	13×14	4 17	4 1	1 1		6 10		
49	,,	,,	I.	M.	6 3	14×16	8 16	8 ..	.. none		7 0		
50	Prescot's	,,	I.	W.	3 4	8×10	8 8	4 ..	.. ..		3 10	ditto	Dirty house.
51	,,	,,	I.	M.	3 3	8×10	7 8	5 ..	.. ..		5 5	ditto	Ditto.
52	,,	,,	I.	M.	6 3	6×9	12 16	5 ..	.. ..		5 5	ditto	Ditto.
53	,,	,,	I.	W.	2 3	10×15	5 13	2 1	.. ..		7 10	ditto	House clean.
54	,,	,,	I.	W.	4 3	10×15	9 14	1 4	.. 2		7 10	ditto	Ditto.
55	,,	,,	I.	M.	4 3	9×12	7 8	4 ..	3 none		6 10	ditto	Ditto.
56	,,	,,	I.	W.	.. 2	6×12	2 2	2 ..	.. ..		2 12	ditto	House dirty; a number of privies, &c. close by the door.
57	Mooor	,,	I.	M.	3 2	14×14	7 12	2 1	.. none		4 0	ditto	A wretched hovel; a midden and privy underneath bed-room.
58	,,	,,	E.	W.	5 5	10×10	10 12	7 ..	1 none		5 10	Fronts the street	House dirty.
59	,,	Rothwell's	I.	M.	4 2	11×11	4 6	3 1	1 1		5 4	Open drain flows into the street	House clean.
60	,,	Banks'	I.	M.	3 6	9×10	7 12	11 ..	1 none		6 0	Open drain flows into the main sewer.	House dirty.

NOTE.—Married and single sleep in the same room without proper means of privacy.

N.B.—E. stands for English; I. for Irish; S. for Scotch; M. for married couples; S. for single; W. for widow.

ROBERT FANNIN, *Superintendent.*

COUNTY CONSTABULARY.— *Ormskirk Division.*

RETURN showing public yards and mode of drainage, also the manner in which the yards belonging to innkeepers are drained.

Yards, &c.	Mode of Drainage.
Aughton-street :—	
Fleece	Drain; empties itself in Aughton-street.
White Bull	Drain; flows into the street.
Smith's	Open drain; flows into the street.
Police-station	Drain; flows into the street.
Parker's	Flows on the surface to the street.
Wilson's	Drained to the street, then flows on the surface.
Bainbridge's	Flows on the surface to the street.
Goss	Ditto.
Greyhound	Drained into the main sewer.
Woods-square	Flows on the surface into the street.
Bull's Head	Ditto.
Banks	Ditto.
Hursts	Ditto.
Bradburns	Ditto.
Miss Parker's	Ditto.
Taylor, blacksmith	Ditto from middens, &c.
Taylor, beerseller	Flows on the surface into the street.
Black Bull	Ditto from middens, &c.
Talbot	Flows on the surface into the street.
Pants, Old Post-office	Flows into the fields.
Church-street :—	
Hutton's	Ditto.
Three Crowns	Drained into the main sewer.
White Lion	Ditto.
Steam-mill	Drained into the fields.
Snigs Foot	Drained to the street, then flows on the surface.
Old Eagle and Child	Drained into the fields.
Blundell's, behind Forrest's	Flows on the surface, from middens, &c.
Balshaw's, Plough	Drained into the main sewer.
Old Charity School	Flows into the fields.
Culshaw's, Bark-house hill	Ditto.
Martins-square	Ditto.
Hauts-lane	Several drains from privies, &c., flows into Burscough-street, very bad smell.
Burscough-street :—	
Pickavant's	Drained to the street, then flows on the surface.
Wood-yard	Flows into the fields; an open drain.
Rising Sun	Open drain flows into the street.
Benson's	Drained from middenstead to the street, and then flows on the surface.
Cloth-hall	Drained into the main sewer.
Gregory's	Open drain flows into the street.
Whitters	Drained into the fields; dirty place.
Buck i' th' Vine	Drained into the main sewer.
Lewis	Flows on the surface into the street.
Swan	Drained into the main sewer.
Sheaf	Ditto.
Moor-street :—	
King's Arms	Ditto.
Black Bear	Flows on the surface to the main sewer.
Golden Lion	Ditto.
Rawsthorne, Charlotte	Ditto.
Queen's Head	Drained into the main sewer.
Anchor	Ditto.
Ship	Ditto.
Slater	Flows on the surface to the main sewer.

ROBERT FANNIN, Superintendent, County Constabulary.

Remarks on the Advantages of Local Government.—The question of efficient local government is one in which the poor are far more deeply concerned than the rich ; heavy rates affect the wealthy, but the state of things which produce heavy money payments from them is productive to the working man of poverty, degradation, extreme misery, sickness, and premature death. It is most suicidal, therefore, in the poor to blindly resist works of improvement ; they should rather aid, to the utmost of their ability, in the work. The honest, hard-working resident looks around and contemplates the vast accumulation of neglected filth which has taken place ; he has also most probably suffered by sickness, either in his own person or in his family ; but his reply to any argument for improvement is probably evaded by throwing all the blame upon " the Irish," or upon " the landlords." That the neglect of landlords and the undue overcrowding of the Irish have brought much sickness upon the town is quite true, but chiefly because there is no local law or locally constituted body to direct and compel proper sanitary works, or to regulate the common lodging-houses. The Public Health Act has been especially framed to remedy these deficiencies ; and yet it is in some places most blindly resisted. It requires, however, to be understood that its application will not be made a matter of force, but of favour. There is neither benefit nor interest in applying the Act but to the rate-payers in general. I would seriously appeal to the working man who resists it, and ask if he can justify such conduct to himself? That the thoughtless and careless owners of ruinous and neglected property should wish to prevent improvement is perhaps only natural ; but even this class would ultimately be benefited by the change, as a ruinous property cannot long be a source of income. The work required to be done to place the town in a proper sanitary condition will not require a first large outlay, and the whole capital required may be borrowed on the security of the rates, so that even the owners of property will not be unduly distressed, as in Liverpool, where the amount required for any work must be paid down in one sum before it is commenced ; and the party has no means of appeal or help, however extravagantly he may consider the work has been laid out.

Abstract of Rating Clauses from the Public Health Act.— The following is an abstract of the rating clauses as embodied in the Public Health Act.

The several clauses of the Public Health Act have been framed with especial care, and the manner of raising the money required and levying the rates necessary are most advantageous and equitable, as the following brief analysis of the rating clauses will show :—

" The rates leviable under the Public Health Act are, first, public rates, and, second, private rates.

"The general district-rate may be levied over the whole or part of a district (ss. 87, 89). Arable, meadow, pasture, and wood land, market-gardens and nursery-grounds, land covered with water, canals, and towing-paths, and land used as a railway, to be assessed upon one-fourth only (s. 88). The general district-rate will consist of the expenses of preliminary inquiry, salaries, &c., of local officers and servants, and certain casual expenses; and all such expenses of executing the Act as are not defrayed by means of any other rate, or out of the district-fund account (see s. 87). The district-fund account will consist of the proceeds arising from the sale of sewage, &c., penalties recoverable by the local Board, and certain other miscellaneous sums received by them.

"*Special District-rates* (s. 86).—Special district-rates will be for making, enlarging, altering, or covering sewers (s. 89). This rate will be levied upon either the whole or part of a district, according to circumstances. But those persons only will be liable whose property has been benefited by the expenses in respect of which the rate is made (s. 86).

"*Water-rate* (s. 93).—This rate will be levied for water supplied for the purposes of domestic use, cleanliness, and house drainage (s. 93). Property to be assessed—the premises supplied (s. 93).

"The rates for public and private improvements may be spread over any period not exceeding 30 years, but must be so distributed as to pay off the expenses in respect of which the rate is made, together with interest not exceeding 5*l*. per cent., within that period (s. 90)."

6th. Estimates will have to be furnished to the rate-payers for all new work undertaken, and before the money can be raised the General Board must be satisfied that such work is well devised, economical, and for the present and permanent advantage of the rate-payers. This is to secure the rate-payer against local incompetency and extravagance, and to furnish at the least cost the best practical information the existing state of scientific knowledge can afford.

Advantages of Act to Landowners.—The advantages to the landowner and farmer will not be less than those furnished to the inhabitants of the town.

1st. Perfect land drainage in the township must in a great measure depend upon a good outfall for the surface-water, and this will be provided for at the least cost after a correct survey has been arranged, and the district examined by a competent surveyor. Intermediate property may require to be cut through; roads will have to be traversed or crossed; and as the local Board will be competent to undertake this, the interest of all parties may be consulted.

2nd. Good roads are necessary for the whole community, and to no class will they be more beneficial than to the farmer. They will enable him to bring manure on his land, and to perform all his operations, where wheeled vehicles are used, at the least cost ; the local board will be surveyors of highways.

PUBLIC MEETING AT THE TOWN-HALL.

Inquiry and Evidence.—At the public inquiry, the *Vicar,* in speaking of the necessity for improvement, described those parts of the town where fever had prevailed, and stated that filth, misery, disease, and immorality were generally found in company.

Mr. *Symonds* confirmed this evidence and stated—

" That fever had not for the last three years been absent from Green-lane, Prescott's-yard, Moor-street, and Old-buildings in Burs-cough-street. The great mass of fever is generated in the low Irish lodging-houses. Thinks if these were drained, supplied with water, cleansed, and regulated, the fever might be abated, if not entirely re-moved. I consider that the cottages in my district are very much overcrowded and neglected ; the refuse stagnates in open middens, cesspools, and on the surface. There should be a local Board to carry out proper improvements and regulations, as such would reduce the sickness.''

Mr. *Joseph Stoner* gave evidence as to the mortality and amount expended in out-door relief, which evidence will be found em-bodied in another part of this Report—

"Thinks a local Board elected by the rate-payers may accomplish much good, if they act with rigid economy. The present condition of the lodging-houses in the town is very bad."

Mr. *William Owen,* relieving officer—

" Invariably found the most relief required in the worst conditioned district. Many places and houses in the town are neglected and filthy in the extreme; has no doubt the pockets of the rate-payers would be materially spared if the drainage and water-supply of the town could be improved."

Mr. *James Palmer* described the levels of the town as favourable for drainage, and stated—

" The condition of the Irish lodging-houses is most abominable. Have frequently, in passing, crossed the road, the smell from them has been so horrid. The parties who build and own some of this property are as wretched as their tenants. Had to survey a district some time since, and could not tread for human refuse ; even where privies exist they are in a most disgusting condition. There is a great want of water ; had counted 117 persons, men, women, and children, waiting for water at one pump."

Mr. *Gould Tilsley* stated —

" That he supplies above 100 families from his own pump."

Mr. *Palmer*—

"There is a lamentable want of water and cleansing ; a water-closet near me passes the refuse out, into, and over the surface-channel, which at all times is a very great nuisance."

Mr. *William Smith* exhibited a bottle of water from his pump as good, but it could scarcely be considered a fair sample, as it was mixed with whisky, or rather had been brought in a whisky-bottle—

" Thinks, although they have fire-engines, there would at present be great difficulty in supplying them with water."

The Rev. *John Atherton Kershaw* stated—

" that he considered there was abundance of water under the town, if landlords were compelled to sink wells and put up pumps."

It was stated in evidence, that the public pumps, so called, have to be paid for by such householders as use them at the rates of 2*s*. or 3*s*. a-year. One ingenious gentleman, who owned a public pump and himself required and used large quantities of water, has the pump so contrived that before the public can raise any for their own use they must pump and maintain his cisterns full.

Mr. *Robert Marsden*, surgeon, stated—

" that all the undrained and dirty parts of the town are very rarely, if ever, free from fever. Considers that there is a great want of water. Much of the present well and pump-water is vitiated so as to be unfit for use. I consider that the houses in my district are very much over crowded. There are no drains; the refuse stands in open cesspools; flows over the surface, and is constantly evaporating, to the serious injury of health. Thinks there should be a local Board to carry out proper works and regulations, as they would reduce the present sickness."

It will almost seem unnecessary so to repeat the evidence as to the condition of the town, but it cannot be too prominent or too much insisted on, as attention and consideration must precede conviction that a remedy is required.

The following statement was handed in, which, as an independent Report on the places named, made by two gentlemen resident in the district, is valuable. Many samples of water were produced with the Report, all of which more or less proved that the wells were in some degree contaminated. But I would direct especial attention to their hardness as shown by the analysis :—

REPORT on a SURVEY of the Courts, Wells, Cesspools, &c., of Aughton-street, Ormskirk, by Messrs. J. Lyon and W. H. Garside, from personal inspection, November 19, 1849.

" Mary Spencer, cowkeeper, is supplied by well-water; the midden is only 5 feet from it.

" — Moorcroft (next door).—A sewer runs under the back yard; the house is on a level with street; very damp. No water supply, and a wet midden inside of front yard wall.

" Roper's-yard.—No water-supply as the pump is out of repair. There are eight cottages and two large cesspools, one of which is 4 yards by 3 yards. The ground is very steep from the back to the street, so that the damp filth drains through the houses.

" Brewery, &c., yard, is in clean order; the surface is kept dry, and there is a good supply of well and rain water.

" Nursery-yard.—There is no water-supply. The refuse of two pigsties and middens at the top of incline ooze through into the dwellings. There is a pool of stagnant water behind the top cottage through which it oozes—it is tainted with decaying vegetables from an adjoining nursery.

" Forshaw's-court or yard.—No supply of water; eight cottages in a *cul-de-sac.* N.B. The front cottagers empty their wet middens through the house.

" Bainbridge's-yard.—A pump and shallow well (3 yards deep); bad water; a horrible pigsty and petty midden. The yard part underdrained into street.

" Forshaw's Brewery.—There is a pump in the yard, but it is out of order.

" Mr. Hugh Owen and Mr. Symonds.—Well-water is moderately clear; slightly alkaline (see sample); surface well drained and clean.

" Monk's-court (next to above).—The well is fouled with defective surface drainage, although the yard is underdrained through the entry to the street.

" Bromley's-court.—Twelve back cottages and three in front are supplied by one pump; the water is slightly flavoured, it is moderately clear. There are only two privies to these 12 cottages.

" Grammar School-courts.—There is a slaughter-house, four pigsties, and a large wet midden on highest part; a currier's shop. All the privies on this property are on the highest land at the back. No water-supply. Constant oozings down yard and entry into street. The front cottages very damp. There is a public well and pump in the street in front of Winrow's shop. The drain from the back court passes between at 5 feet distance from the pump.

" Police Station.—Supply of water, full of what appears animalcula; has an alkaline taste.

" Miss Rogerson's and two cottages at back.—No water; two pigsties; drained on surface.

" Mr. Sherlock and next house.—Pump out of order; get tea-water from the White Bull.

" Joseph Smith, veterinary surgeon.—Good and plentiful supply of well-water. The surface tolerably clean and dry.

" White Bull Inn-yard.—A pump which supplies a great number of families. It is 9 yards deep, and 2 yards of water; good water, but full of mites or animalcula; yard is drained down gateway; part under and part surface.

" Fleece inn-yard.—One pump to well; 9 yards deep with two yards of water; full of animalcula. There is a large vault (covered) as a receptacle for all kinds of refuse, wet and dry, half way up the yard.

" These comprise nearly all the east side of Aughton-street.

" *West side of Aughton-street.*

" Garside's.—Well-water very bad.

" Talbot Inn.—Ditto, rather worse.

" Gaslight Company's well.—Very bad.

" Bostock's beer-house.—Yard well very bad.

" There is a wet midden in Campbell's yard which oozes through into the common passage of the gasworks through Bostock's yard.

" — Murphy, cowkeeper, has a shallow well; the water is tinged and flavoured; scanty supply. No privies to cottages in front; a heap of filth at the back. Horse, cow, pig, and petty midden heaped up next front wall, continually oozing through the wall over the parapet.

" The whole town stands on a thick bed of porous sand, which is a fertile source of infection to the wells, by the infiltration of impurities through the surface, and affords ready relief to partially-stopped sewers by absorption into its spongy substance. Some of the wells on the east side of Aughton-street had a flavour very similar to what would result from a few grains of Epsom salts dissolved in a tumbler of pure water. Some had a ferruginous taste.

(Signed)   " Joseph Lyon.
" W. H. Garside.

" To Robert Rawlinson, Esq."

Existing Sewers and Drains.—There is no general system of sewerage in the town; such as have been made are isolated; and they are as imperfect in their action as they have been originally void of design. House-drains cannot be said to exist. The following statement describing the existing sewers was handed in by

William Aspinwall, late surveyor of Ormskirk, who superintended the construction of the sewers. He stated—

" There is a small square sough * from Thomas Twist's, in Aughton-street, down to Fairbridge's, in Aughton-street. No public sewer, except one of about twenty yards, which empties itself into the open street under the Fish-stones in Aughton-street. There is also a sewer (18 inches in diameter) from Chapel-lane, near the Methodist Chapel, and another from Rough-lane, meeting Chapel-lane sewer, down to the junction of Moor-street, which empties itself under the railway bridge; and another from thence of 18 inches on each side of Moor-street, forming a junction opposite John Collison's shop, and from thence to the Cross. In Burscough-street a sewer from Buck-i'-th'-Vine to the Cross (18 inches diameter), which meets the Moor-street sewer, forming a junction with a short sewer up Church-street (2 feet diameter), down William Owen's gateway, and emptying itself into the open fields. There is another very short one at the top of Church-street emptying itself at the bottom of Charity School-yard. Another short one from Mr. Palmer's office to the bottom of Burscough-street, emptying itself into an open drain."

With respect to the drainage, Mr. *Welsby* stated—

" I have paid some attention to the sewerage and drainage of the town, and I should say that two-thirds of the streets (irrespective of the public highways) possess no public sewer, and nine-tenths of the courts, yards, and houses are entirely destitute of covered drains, the refuse flowing over the surface into the channels of the public streets, where it either evaporates or passes on to the outskirts; the principal

---

* " *Sough*," a local name for sewer or drain.

outlet receptacle being a brook dividing the parish of Ormskirk from Aughton. More than two-thirds of the town drainage stagnates and becomes, especially during the summer months, a most abominable nuisance. There is a sewer down a portion of Moor-street, but even here there are few private drains; and the surface of the footwalks and streets are contaminated with all sorts of liquid abominations flowing from surcharged cesspools and middens. For want of proper connexion, fall and regular flushing, the sewers frequently become the greatest nuisance in the town.

" *Aughton-street* is not sewered, and is very imperfectly paved. The land on each side slopes from the back towards the street; the overflow from the cesspools and middens consequently finds its way over the surface and at times covers the whole street with a foul sediment, the smell of which is frequently so bad that persons residing in other parts of the town will go considerably out of their direct course rather than pass down this street. The lower portion, which constitutes one of the main entrances into the town, consists principally of common lodging-houses, occupied by Irish. Many of these places have no sort of accommodation at the back, and the street is regularly made the receptacle of that which is alike offensive to sight and smell.

" The public lodging-houses are a great nuisance, perhaps one of the greatest pests we have, and I have no doubt they in a great degree caused the excessive mortality we have suffered for the last two or three years. Disease originates in these abodes of squalor and misery, but does not always confine its ravages to the place of its birth. Many families experienced the truth of this in the summer of 1847, and had great reason to regret the want of such a remedy as the Public Health Act is calculated to afford in moderating, if not entirely preventing, such a calamity as this town then endured."

REMARKS.—The poor inhabitants retain the refuse of a whole year upon and about their premises for the purpose of selling it to the farmers, utterly regardless of the terrible cost they pay in their health by such a proceeding. It is from large heaps of refuse, stored until fermentation takes place, that disease in its most deadly form is generated; and during the prevalence of any severe epidemic, persons living in the vicinity of such accumulations are suddenly struck down as by the most rapid acting poison. Such has been the case in many places during the prevalence of cholera.

Letter describing the Sanitary State of the Town.—The following letter, which was laid before me at the request of Mr. Lyon, treats at considerable length the several heads of the inquiry; and being the opinion of a gentleman resident in the neighbourhood, well acquainted with the town, and wishful to assist in bringing about improvement, it is peculiarly valuable :—

" Rose-hill, Aughton, Dec. 30, 1848.
" Respecting the adoption of the Health of Towns Act for Ormskirk, I have no hesitation in saying, that if there is one town in her Majesty's dominions that calls more loudly for sanitary measures than

any other, *Ormskirk is that town.* In the first place, the very few sewers now existing in it are rather nuisances than otherwise, and for want of free exits become depositories of mud and filth. One example is to be found in Aughton-street, the level of which is indented or depressed about one-fourth of its length, and is lower than the exit at the brook side. The said outlet is entirely choked up by the brook water in heavy rains; and, as a necessary consequence, the street is flooded with water and mud boiling up through the sewer grates, leaving a deposit on the surface impregnated with animal and vegetable refuse, which, by the combined action of the sun and air, is constantly giving off noxious gases; and, to add to the nuisance, part of the sewers are carried along under the parapets, close to the front walls of the houses. Several of the cottages in the same street being without privies, the necessary consequence is the discharge of the contents of utensils, &c., into the open street. In the next place, the back premises of the whole of the east side of Aughton-street are much higher than the street, and inclining thereto. The middens and cesspools (mostly mere holes dug in the ground) are the common receptacles, abounding in all kinds of floating, festering abominations. The liquid portion is conveyed by filtration, assisted by rains, through the ground; and infect the wells, in some instances, so as to colour the water about the tint of very pale sherry. Some few of the wells yield usable water, which is, doubtless, owing to the ground, to some extent around, being raised high enough to carry off the surface-water so quickly as to prevent absorption. To give any adequate idea of the filthy, confined, and unventilated state of a very large portion of the back premises in the town, language fails; personal inspection alone can suffice. Another source of defiling the streets is traceable to the cattle fairs held twice a year, the space of time between any of which is scarcely sufficient to obliterate the effects of the preceding one. Most of the wells, both private and public, are shallow; and a good supply of water to extinguish fires in the town is a thing not to be looked for, which renders the services of the three powerful fire-engines, with an efficient staff, comparatively worthless. Rain water is extensively used for culinary purposes, and in an unfiltered state; consequently, it is impregnated with all the usual gaseous impurities condensed on roofs, and metallic taint acquired in its passage through leaden gutters, pipes, &c. Indeed, I have heard it asserted that many persons in the town suffer from diseases traceable to the use of bad water.

"With respect to the common lodging-houses, which are chiefly resorted to by the poorest classes and Irish harvest men, a very strict surveillance will be required to keep them in moderately decent order. The Act only gives authority to inspect them between the hours of eleven and four o'clock (see Sec. 66), a period when nearly all the inmates are dispersed to follow their various occupations; nevertheless, great step will be gained by enforcing cleanliness only.

"Having touched upon several of the proximate causes of the unhealthy state of Ormskirk, I now beg to submit my views of remedial measures, which, in my humble opinion, are indispensable to the public health of the town generally. First, the main streets to be laid with sewers sufficiently large, and of proper levels and inclinations, to convey away all liquid impurities arising from every source, and into which a drain or drains from every house, shop, or court be laid; sufficient mains laid in every street, through which to get a plentiful supply of water from plugs and stand-pipes to water the streets, to flush the sewers, courts, &c.; also for baths, washhouses, &c., a daily supply of pure water for every house, cottage, or premises of every kind requiring it. The only effectual mode of accomplishing these would be by a complete waterworks plant, either under the immediate direction of the Local Board, or by a joint-stock company sanctioned by them.

" It is thought that the same strata which furnish the bath springs, run under the town itself; so that, by sinking a well with a spacious chamber in the precincts of the town, abundance of the purest water may be raised by an engine high enough to deliver it at the top of the highest building, and, what would be very desirable, to keep the mains full at a pressure for extinguishing fires in any part of the town. It may be observed, that by keeping the surface of the town clean and well drained, the present wells would yield purer water; but even *that* could not be thoroughly effected without a liberal supply from other sources. It is worthy of remark that there is not a *bath in the whole town*, not even in the public dispensary, owing entirely to the want of a water-supply. It cannot be a matter of surprise that the poorer classes fall into dirty habits, which of themselves engender disease, intemperance, and a host of evils equally dangerous and destructive—all for lack of a proper supply of that simple and invaluable element, pure water.

" There are many minor matters which will be amply remedied by the provisions in the Health of Towns Act, that it is not necessary for me to enumerate or dilate upon in this slight sketch. I shall, however, be truly gratified if the few remarks above will, in the least degree, contribute to forward the sanitary movement now being promoted for the benefit of Ormskirk. Should it be successful, you will be entitled to the grateful acknowledgments of the whole community for the prominent, indefatigable, and effective part you have and are sustaining to confer a lasting boon on the present and future generations of your townsmen and neighbours.

" In conclusion, I have only to say that I view the Health of Towns Act, as applied to Ormskirk, as a powerful prospective engine for its physical and moral regeneration.

(Signed)   " JOSEPH LYON.

" To William Welsby, Esq."

PERSONAL INSPECTION.—I made a personal inspection of the town and district in company with the gentlemen here named :— The Rev. E. G. G. Hornby; William Welsby, Esq.; Charles P. Symonds, Esq.; R. M. Marsden, Esq.; Mr. Joseph Stoner; and Mr. Thomas Kershaw.

REMARKS.—*Church-street.*—Most imperfect drainage and water supply. On the west side, the house drainage passes over the surface into the brook bounding the township. This brook receives all the refuse of Aughton-street, Moor-street, Chapel-lane, part of Burscough-street, and Church-street. This brook is at all times most foul; but especially so, and most offensive, in summer. The whole of Aughton street has a surface-drainage only, and at times, for want of proper cleansing, is exceedingly foul. A large cottage population from Church-street, Barkhouse-hill, Green-lane, Haunt's-lane, and neighbourhood, have to fetch water from a well* on the road side, several hundred yards distant. In Haunt's-lane there is a wretched property. The houses are crowded together, the surface is unformed and un-paved; pigsties and open middens crowd the place; in some in-stances they are close under the windows. Such privies as exist are in a most filthy condition. The district is principally in-habited by Irish, who invariably crowd their houses with lodgers. During the harvest season the crowding is said to be "fearful." Fever is constant amongst these people; but during this over-crowding it breaks out with extreme virulence.

The Guardians, about two years ago, erected a temporary fever hospital or shed near the town. Upwards of 70 fever cases have been in this place at one time, and other cases have, at the same time, been attended at the cost of the parish in the lodging-houses. The removal to the fever shed has been attended with the most beneficial results, but during the two years the same individuals and families have been several times admitted.

Burscough-street.—A sewer from the upper portion opens on to the surface at the lower end into an open drain. All the water for the yards must pass out on to the surface of the street. There are about four or five water-closets in the town, and three of these pass the contents into the channel of the street.

There are no cottage-garden allotments in the district. Much of the land belongs to the Right Honourable the Earl of Derby. It was formerly let on lease for lives; at present it is leased for 75 years.

The cottage gardens at Alnwick, set apart and let to the poor of that town by his Grace the Duke of Northumberland, on the condition that they shall be properly cultivated by spade labour, appear to be highly appreciated. There is little doubt some such arrangement would be appreciated by the working men in Ormskirk.

WATER-SUPPLY.—The present water-supply is from pumps and wells; some portions of the town are said to be abundantly supplied, whilst other districts, and these the poorest, are deficient. At the inquiry there were many conflicting, and some contradictory statements made as to the necessity of a public and general supply being required. Mr. Thomas Worsley put in a statement show-

---

* The ' iron dish well,' so called because there used to be an iron ladle chained to the well.

ing "that there are upwards of 200 wells and pumps * to a population of 4891, or about 1100 householders." This is one well or pump on the average to each 24 persons, or 5 householders. But as the better class houses have their pumps in their own yards, many cottagers are without any certain supply. Most of the wells yield water which cannot be used for drinking or culinary purposes, so that the effective supply of that which is even locally considered good water is very small.

The cost of sinking a well, and fixing a pump complete, is said to be about 21*s.* each yard in depth the well is sunk, and the local wells were said to vary from 7 to 30 yards in depth, and that the average depth was about 10 yards. This will give an average cost of 10*l.* 10*s.* for each well and pump as the first outlay. There is the annual cost for maintenance and repairs to be added :—

200 pumps, first cost, each 10*l.* 10*s.* . 2100*l.*

	£	s.	d.
2100*l.* capital at 5 per cent., is . . .	105	0	0 annually
Annual repairs, say	50	0	0
Annual per centage on tubs, cans, pots, buckets, and labour to fetch and retain the water, say	50	0	0
Annual expenditure . . .	£205	0	0

Remarks on the Advantage of a full Supply of Water.—A full supply of water necessarily implies that each householder shall have at his or her command, without labour, as incurred by pumping, abundance for all purposes : a supply which would be more than equal to a separate pump to or in each house. The experience of those towns where a full supply of water has been given is, that it may be furnished to each cottage at an annual charge of 1*s.* each quarter, or 4*s.* a year. This is the case in Preston, Bury, Bolton, Carlisle, and other towns. No extent of pump accommodation can equal a well regulated constant high-pressure system, as water may be used and supplied for other than household purposes. Sewers and drains require for their proper action and cleansing that water may be used in abundance, without labour. If the mains and branches are constantly charged at high-pressure, the surface of yards, passages, streets, footwalks and channels may be daily cleansed by means of the hose, to the great increase of health and comfort to the inhabitants, and the reduction of scavenging rates. The cost of fire-engines will be superseded, and much greater security from fire be attained, as there will be water in abundance under pressure,

---

* Evidence was brought forward to show that there are only 85 wells and pumps, and that not more than ten of these are fit for use.

and consequently self-acting at a moment's notice. A company or establishment, to supply water on a large scale, may pump and supply it at rates from 1*d.* to 6*d.* each thousand gallons.* The working cost to lift 80,000 gallons 100 feet is 1*s.*, where a Cornish engine is used. To pump water into an ordinary water-cart by hand-labour will cost several shillings each thousand gallons.

As many persons at the inquiry were opposed to the formation of a company for the supply of the town generally, it may be well to examine their arguments in detail. The fact that the present supply is most inadequate in certain parts of the town was not denied, and the argument used was "compel landlords to sink wells, or deepen those they have." If this should be done, how would the account with the town stand? If 200 pumps are deducted from 1,100 householders or tenements, there will remain 900 without either well or pump. Make it imperative that every 4 householders out of the 900 should have one pump, and there must be 250 additional pumps provided. This would require a capital of 2625*l.* to be expended in the first instance; involving an annual expenditure, in interest at 5 per cent., of 131*l.* 5*s.*, with, at the lowest possible computation, 100*l.* additional for maintenance and repairs. Add these sums to the previous estimate of 205*l.*, and the whole annual expenditure will be 436*l.* 5*s.*, which represents a capital of 8725*l.*: and this for an imperfect, inefficient, and, in many instances—as shown by Mr. Lyon—water highly charged with offensive matter from drains, cesspools, or other local vitiating causes.

Public pumps and public wells are not only most expensive and inefficient, but they are the cause of much ill feeling, and, in many instances, immorality. Children and servant-girls are obliged to stand and wait at the well or pump where quarrels are taking place, too frequently with a use of most improper language.

An inefficient supply of good and soft water induces the use of rain-water cisterns. These alone must be purchased and maintained at a cost more than would pay the rental of a full supply from any properly regulated establishment.

Remarks on the Impurities of shallow Wells in a Town.— Ormskirk, as stated, is built on the new red sandstone formation. The regular stratification is covered by alluvial deposit, varying in its character; it may be sand, gravel, marl, clay, peat, or a mixture of these. This stratum is generally full of water, which is supplied from the surface according as the ground is more or less porous, and hence the great difference observable in

---

* At this present time the Manchester Corporation have entered into a contract to supply Salford with a million gallons of water per day at the rate of 3*d.* each thousand gallons.

wells not far apart. Those sunk in sand or gravel will be liable to contamination from middens, drains, and cesspools, and from graveyards, if within their vicinity. This is proved most palpably by the chemist, and inferentially by the alteration which is found to take place in certain wells and pumps after their first formation. Those wells sunk through clay, or into the rock, will not be so liable to this contamination, and some such may probably escape it, but they are excessively hard and wasteful.* The fact that any water is clear, bright, and sparkling is no true indication of its purity; such a water may even be charged with offensive and dangerous impurities. One of the most essential requisites to a town is an abundant supply of soft and pure water. No pains should be spared to secure this; and by means of one establishment, well managed and regulated, it may be supplied at a cost which shall be cheap to the occupier of a cottage.

GASWORKS AND FIRE-ENGINE ESTABLISHMENT.—The gasworks were established in 1833; they are not under the powers of any Act, but were established by a private company. The works are situated in Aughton-street.

The gas is made from cannel coal, and is charged 7s. 6d. per 1000 feet to general consumers; and 6s. per annum is charged for the meter.

At present there are 47 public lights; they are lighted from the 1st of September to the 1st of May, from sunset to sunrise, with the exception of four days before full moon, the full, and three days after. The lamps are supplied by meter, and the gas is charged 7s. 6d. each thousand feet; the cost for gas to each lamp for the time stated is about 36s. The town authorities or inspectors find and maintain the posts and lamps. The company also charge 8s. for each seven nights for lighting, cleaning, and extinguishing the lamps.

The gas and fire-engine department is managed by seven inspectors, elected for three years (under the powers of the Lighting and Watching Act), on the 1st of November each year; unless this should be Sunday, when the election takes place the day after. The annual rate levied is 4½d. in the pound, which produces about 170l.; the accounts are submitted annually to the rate-payers for inspection and sanction, with an estimate of the probable outlay for the coming year, which is submitted to the vote. The rate is levied 4½d. on house property, and 1½d. on land. About 1d. of this rate is required to maintain the fire-engines, of which there are three; these engines were purchased with money raised by private subscriptions and a donation from Lord Derby's jury of the court-leet.

The cost of the fire-engine establishment is as under :—

---

* See Analysis by Dr. Lyon Playfair, with remarks on this subject.

Rent of engine-house per annum .	.£7	0	0
Secretary	. 4	0	0
Treasurer	. 2	0	0
Rent of room for business . . .	. 1	0	0
12 engine-men, retained at 10s. 6d. .	. 6	6	0
1 principal	. 5	0	0
Annual expenditure . .	£25	6	0

The rate is collected by the overseer, who is paid for his trouble out of the general fund 4l. per annum.

To obtain powers to open the streets to lay their mains, the gas company passed the following resolution at a meeting of the gas committee, held October 3rd, 1833 :—

" Inasmuch as the poor cottagers would be liable to the rate in proportion to their rental, the company, at a meeting of the shareholders, unanimously determined to relieve the poor tenant by paying the gas rate upon all cottages of 5l. annual rent and under.

(Signed) " LAWRENCE WRIGHT,
" Secretary to the Company."

There have been frequent disputes with the inspectors chosen by the rate-payers and the company as to the meaning of this clause: the inspectors contending that all cottages of 5l. annual rental, and under, were exempted ; the company insisting on the term " poor cottagers."

REMARKS AND SUGGESTIONS.—The whole of a town should be well, regularly, and cheaply lighted. Lamps should not alone be confined to the public streets, but they should also be placed in all the back streets, lanes, courts, yards, and alleys, and for some distance outside of the town. A light would frequently prevent much mischief, immorality, and even theft. If possible, the local Board, when formed, ought to purchase the present gasworks, that they may be managed for the sole use and benefit of the rate-payers, as in Manchester, where an annual income of upwards of 35,000l. is realized for the improvement of the town, all of which would be lost to the inhabitants if the works were in the hands of a private company. One engineer or surveyor, one clerk, and one collector, may, with advantage, transact all the business of the local Board, supposing they possessed the gasworks, waterworks, and formed, controlled, and repaired the streets, roads, sewers, drains, and performed the cleansing and regulating throughout the township.

BURIAL-GROUNDS.—The present burial-ground, which is the churchyard, is nearly full, and a new cemetery should be provided. Burials have taken place within the church, and at this time there are large square vaults in which several coffins rest, the vault being covered with timber platform-doors hinged to the floor.

STREETS AND ROADS UNDER THE GENERAL HIGHWAY ACT. —The streets are repaired and cleansed under the superintendence of a surveyor appointed annually in public vestry by the rate-payers. A rate of 6*d.* in the pound is levied annually on 10,946*l.* The East Lancashire Railway Company also pay 25*l.* annually for the right of a level crossing over Dyer's-lane. The whole rate and income is as under :—

	£.	s.	d.
Annual rate from 10,946*l.* at 6*d.* in the pound .	273	13	0
Received from East Lancashire Railway Company	25	0	0
	£298	13	0

Out of this sum the surveyor is paid for his services 15*l.* annually ; the collector is paid 7*l.* 17*s.* 6*d.* for collecting the rate and making the book.

The streets are in general paved with boulders, and most of the gutters and footwalks are formed with the same material. The present surveyor has served several years ; his business is a tallow-chandler. There are several streets which have never been formed or paved ; Haunts-lane and the new road leading from Moor-street to Lydiate-lane, for instance.

The whole of the cleansing and scavenging is done by hand ; no regular establishment is kept for this purpose, and frequently the surveyor allows the poorer class of rate-payers, when out of employment, to work off the amount of their rate in the streets. The paving and repairing is generally executed by contract.

VILLA RESIDENCES.—There are many beautiful sites for villa residences near the town, at Scarth-hill, the Rough, Greetby Hill, and Aughton. The distance by railway is only eleven miles from Liverpool, and when the railway company consult their own interests they will grant cheap annual tickets, which will be alike beneficial to themselves, to the merchants of Liverpool, and to the landowners in the neighbourhood of Ormskirk.

This extension of a better class residence may be made mutually beneficial to the poor as to the rich. The landowners must aid and assist to improve the town for the sake of their adjoining estates, that the stigma of excessive disease may be removed from the district, as, so improved, nature has provided a subsoil and atmosphere which ought to produce a state of health equal to any in the kingdom.

SLAUGHTER-HOUSES.—There are several slaughter-houses in the town, generally situated behind the butchers' shops ; they are crowded amongst the dwelling-houses and have no proper means of drainage ; large middens, on to which the blood and garbage is thrown, exist near them ; and, in general, their condition is such as to be a nuisance to the surrounding inhabitants. The blood, if washed away, necessarily, with the water, flows out into the street and over the surface.

Near the steam-mill in Church-street there is a knacker's yard, which was much complained of.

Suggestions with respect to Slaughter-houses.—The removal of slaughter-houses from crowded localities is most desirable, and in all well-regulated towns this will be accomplished. By sec. 62, the "local Board may provide slaughter-houses, and make bye-laws with respect to all slaughter-houses." Sec. 61 enacts that "slaughter-houses be registered." All slaughter-houses will require to be perfectly drained, and to be provided with a full supply of water on the premises.

1st. In each slaughter-house there should be means of thorough ventilation provided at the ceiling or highest part of the roof. A slit-like opening round the whole room, or louvers, afford the best means of free and perfect ventilation, as by such arrangement the outlet will be diffuse. Windows in side walls or square openings in the ceiling or roof do not act so freely or efficiently as a narrow opening continued round the room, and placed as high as practicable.

2nd. The floors should be paved with material impervious to wet, or with such as would be easily washed; there should be no open joints or rough inequalities on the surface. Asphalte will make a floor impervious to wet; and fire-bricks on edge, set in cement, or hydraulic mortar, will probably make the best floor which can be laid down, as the surface may be washed perfectly clean, and the bricks will not wear slippery beneath the feet of the cattle.

3rd. The lower portion of the room may, with much advantage, be lined with fire-bricks set in cement or good mortar, and jointed with the best cement. This surface should not be plastered, but finished so as to allow of its being washed with the floor. The walls should be frequently washed, and all the upper portions of the slaughter-house be limewashed occasionally. In the construction of slaughter-houses, every portion of their structure which is liable to come into contact with the meat should be of such material as will easily wash.

4th. All refuse should be removed from the premises at short intervals. In no instance should any portion of the manure, offal, blood, or refuse of any kind, remain longer than two days; but their removal at shorter intervals will benefit alike the butcher and the public.

5th. Cesspools or covered middens should not in any instance be allowed, where liquid and solid refuse, though covered from sight, would be not less injurious in its action.

Properly ventilated, cleansed, and regulated slaughter-houses will be of the utmost advantage and value to the butcher, as the slightest taint of corruption generates corruption, and gaseous emanations from decaying animal and vegetable refuse are most injurious to life, and rapidly taint fresh meat.

In the construction of slaughter-houses, every portion of their structure which is liable to come into contact with the meat should be of such material as will easily wash.

ROOM-TENEMENTS AND COMMON LODGING-HOUSES.—In dealing with the evils attendant upon these places as they at present exist, mere rules and regulations will be of little avail unless active measures are adopted to provide better accommodation for the poor whom the law will turn out from all rooms and dwellings not in accordance with the requirements of the Act; and it will be a subject for the serious consideration of the local Board as to whether they should not provide model cottages and model lodging-houses in the first instance, not on mere charitable considerations, but as a source of reasonable income, and to set an example in the neighbourhood, by showing that the poorest dwelling may be provided with all the means of comfort and health, and at the same time yield a profitable income as an investment, and directly and indirectly relieve the poor's-rates. Constructions such as the model houses for families and the model lodging-houses in London may be adapted to the situation and requirements of the district.*

The regulation of lodging-houses and tenements will require constant and active attention; but it is a subject of such weighty import, connects itself so intimately with the health and morality of the people, that to perform other sanitary works and neglect this would be of little avail. At present they are a direct money tax upon the rate-payer, frequently to a greater amount than the whole rent paid for them, so that it would actually be cheaper to provide proper lodgings free of cost than to allow them to remain as they are.

REMARKS AND OBSERVATIONS ON TILES, TILE-MAKING, AND THEIR USE FOR LAND AND TOWN DRAINS.—Earthenware tiles have recently been brought into extensive use for land drainage, for street and house drains, and even for the main outlet sewers of towns. Through the indefatigable labours of Edwin Chadwick, Esq., and others, this subject has been thoroughly investigated, theoretically and practically; and the result of both experiment and practice is, that pipes of comparatively small diameter serve better the purposes of drainage than the hitherto large and much more expensive brick and stone sewers and drains. The power of water to remove solids and semi-solids is in proportion to the volume, head, or vertical depth, and the gradient down which it is made to flow. Thus, all these things being the same, a pipe of 4 inches diameter will drain any ascertained area within its capacity better than a larger sewer; as the power of water to remove solids and semi-solids sent in from house and yard drainage will be

---

* A cheap work on the dwellings of the labouring classes has recently been published by Henry Roberts, F.S.A., which contains much valuable information on this most important subject.

greater the more nearly this pipe is graduated to the volume of
water to be sent through it.   There are other considerations with
respect to house drains which dictate a minimum diameter of
pipe, rather than the volume of water to be passed from any one
house : as, for instance, the drain from any one water-closet should
not be less than 4 inches internal diameter.   But one such 4-inch
pipe may have several 4-inch branches, and will remove or take
off the drainage of several houses.   Experiment and actual experience have proved that such a pipe will be preserved in work, open
and clean from refuse sediment ; whilst all past experience has
proved that the more expensive house drains of 2 feet, 18 inches,
and even those of 12 inches diameter, inevitable choke with
sediment and refuse, and ultimately become blocked entirely up ;
because the volume of water is spread out over a wider area in
drains of these larger dimensions, and the whole solid refuse is
deposited in the drain, and much of the thin and stagnant sheet of
water is evaporated.   Should there be the slightest imperfection
in the traps or junctions of the drains, this foul and most unwholesome gas is gradually but constantly passed into the house or
houses, alike destructive of health and comfort, and tending to
produce premature death.

The discharges of water through pipes of small diameter, and
laid at varying angles of fall, have been recently tested, and the
result of the experiments has falsified the formulæ of all the
mathematicians.   A pipe 6 inches internal diameter, laid at an
inclination of 1 in 60, and the head just filled, will discharge
75 cubic feet of water per minute ; and in the length of 100 feet
the outer sectional area of the pipe occupied is reduced to 1-5th.
The whole volume of water such a pipe will pass through it in
24 hours is equal to 675,000 gallons, or a depth of rainfall
amounting to 2-10ths of an inch over an area of upwards of 14
acres, supposing the whole of this water to leave the ground in
that time.   Such an amount of rainfall is more than the daily
average of the wettest month, and little more than one-half the
rainfall is found to flow off the land, much of it being absorbed
or evaporated.   This volume of water will pass through a single
line of pipe without branch feeders ; but by a proper junction of
branch pipes a much larger volume will be delivered through
the main pipe, as the velocity is increased with the volume up to
a certain point.

House and town drains have but one principal purpose to serve,
namely, the perfect and speedy removal of all liquid, solid, and
semisolid refuse to some common outlet or reservoir, where it may
be dealt with for agricultural purposes, without creating a nuisance
or in any way endangering health.   Land-drains have two most
important purposes to serve, and these are, not only to remove all
excess of moisture, but also to conduct atmospheric air into the
soil.   To drain off the water is one purpose, to admit air is of

equal importance. That the drains may perform this two-fold operation perfectly, the main outfalls should be well chosen, their inclination or gradients the best the county will afford, the form and capacity of the drains such that they will not only pass off the water but remove all sand and silt which may find its way into them.

Tiles are made in the district at the following prices :—

THE PRICES of TILES at Fazakerley's Works, near Blythe Hall, about two miles from Ormskirk, are as follows :—

	Diameter.	(Each tile 12 inches in length.)				£.	s.	d.
Pipes	1½ In.	per Thousand	.	.	.	0	17	0
	2 In.	do.	.	.	.	1	0	0
	2½ In.	do.	.	.	.	1	4	0
	4 In.	do.	.	.	.	2	10	0
	2 In. by 2½, with a flat bottom		.	.	1	3	0
Tiles	2 In.	per Thousand	.	.	.	1	0	0
With one side open	2½ In.	do.	.	.	.	1	3	0
	3 In.	do.	.	.	.	1	6	0
	4 In.	do.	.	.	.	1	15	0
	6 In.	do.	.	.	.	2	5	0

THE Number of TILES, 12 inches long, required to drain one Acre of of Land, statute measure ; and the Number of Lineal Roods in an Acre of the said measure of Eight Yards to the Rood, are as follows :—

				Tiles.	Lineal Roods.
4 Yards apart	.	.		3630	151¼
5 ,,	.	.		2904	121
6 ,,	.	.		2420	100¾
7 ,,	.	.		2074	86½
8 ,,	.	.		1815	75½
9 ,,	.	.		1613	67¼
10 ,,	.	.		1452	60½
11 ,,	.	.		1320	55
12 ,,	.	.		1210	50½

REMEDIAL MEASURES AND NEW WORKS PROPOSED.—The whole of the evidence furnished during the inquiry, abstracts of which are given in this Report, will, I trust, make it plain to the understanding of the most obstinate opponent to sanitary measures in general, that some form of regulation, calculated to work improvement, is imperatively required in Ormskirk to reduce the appalling mortality which has recently settled upon the town. Every individual inhabitant is most vitally interested in the questions, How can this excessive rate of death be reduced, and the health of the working man be improved? How can the increased poor's-rates be reduced, and how can a cheap and efficient form of local government be obtained?

Sewerage and House Drainage.—It is a fact abundantly established, that the lower animals even do not thrive in an atmosphere of their own decomposing excrements; how then need we look to secure health if the poor are allowed to exist surrounded by an external atmosphere vitiated to the highest degree, and, from excessive overcrowding within their houses, an atmosphere is inhaled which is absolutely poisonous? The wonderful mechanism of the human body does in a measure adapt itself to the condition in which it is placed, and hence life struggles on where otherwise all would be desolation or death. Any person unused to such a mode of life, and passing from a fresh atmosphere into one of the overcrowded rooms of a common lodging-house, could not breathe it with impunity one half hour—scarcely five minutes. The exhalations from the foul, undrained surface, the adjoining privy and cesspool, or the large open midden, are imperceptibly loading the air with gases which in their concentrated form would destroy life with the rapidity of a lightning stroke. They are identical with that confined sewer gas which, on a recent occasion, killed the men at Pimlico who ventured into it.

In every town which I have inspected—Dover, Portsmouth, Fareham, Birmingham, Wolverhampton, Bilston, Willenhall, Wedensfield, Stoke-upon-Trent, Hanley and Shetton, Felton, Penrith, Carlisle, Newcastle-upon-Tyne, Gateshead, Sunderland, Morpeth, Alnwick; Berwick-upon-Tweed, and numerous villages —I have invariably found that excess of filth and excess of disease are in connexion.

In Alnwick the late terrible visitation of cholera found its victims in their appropriate quarters, living upon a damp, highly vitiated, and undrained subsoil, and in close contact with large middens. In the village of Wreckenton extreme overcrowding and filth prevailed; here the cholera carried off one in seven of the entire population.

The fact, however, that cholera and filth are connected was shown at Alnwick, in the case of premises locally known as "the Tunnel," in a most marked degree. This place was known to be the worst in all respects in the whole town; the houses are crowded together and are most ruinous; each room is let off as a separate tenement to tinkers and vagrants, who overcrowd, as in all other places; and the premises were filthy to the extreme.

Mr. John Davidson, surgeon, in anticipation of the cholera, prevailed upon the Guardians to take forcible possession, which they did for a time. The solid and liquid refuse was removed, the yard surfaces were cleansed with water, the rooms were fumigated and lime-washed, and all was completed about one fortnight before the actual outbreak of cholera took place, which it did suddenly in the night betwixt the 22nd and 23rd of September. Upwards of 140 deaths took place out of a population of 6000 within 30 days, but not one death occurred in the place which had been so cleansed. The fair inference is, that could the whole town have been treated as was the Tunnel, because it was the worst and filthiest locality, these 140 cholera deaths might have been prevented, though the improvement would only have been temporary.

A cheap and permanent remedy is alone to be found in proper

sewers and house-drains, with the other sanitary works and regulations as detailed.

Street and house drainage will alone imperceptibly remove the
refuse from every house, and if this is done in a proper manner,
the first cost even will not be oppressive. But the Public Health
Act wisely provides that the local Board shall have power to
raise the capital required on loan, which is to be repaid by annual
rates within the period of thirty years.

The whole of Ormskirk may be sewered and drained with
earthenware tiles; so that every street shall have its appropriate
sewer, and every house, yard, and sink, its proper drain trapped
complete, which shall not cost more than 2500*l*. Back drainage
should as much as possible be adopted, as affording the cheapest
and easiest means of taking away all liquid refuse. Each house,
yard, and alley, should have its appropriate drain laid at such a
depth as will perfectly drain the deepest cellar. A tile pipe of
4 inches internal diameter, will effectually drain several houses;
and such pipes have been laid complete, including syphon traps,
for 1*s*. 6*d*. each lineal yard. This, on an average, will not cost
more, in the first instance, than 12*s*. 6*d*. to each house. Soil-pan
apparatus may be fixed complete, in existing privies, for 20*s*.;
and they may be provided and fitted up for a first cost of 2*l*. 10*s*.
to each house, which, with the drains, will be represented by an
annual payment a little more than one halfpenny per week.

APPLICATION OF SEWAGE REFUSE TO AGRICULTURE.—The
whole of the sewage refuse of the town may be applied to the land
in the district with singular advantages. Much of it may be used
direct from the tank, or tanks, in a liquid form; other portions
may be " deodorized," perfectly free from smell, the solid matter
being made perfectly inodorous and capable of being removed in
sacks by any conveyance. Parties may be found who will contract
for the whole at a certain annual rental; supplying at their own
cost the necessary machinery and deodorizing mixtures, if the
local board will grant a lease for 21 years, terminable every seven
years. The board may, however, retain the possession and
management in their hands for the benefit of the ratepayers.

WATER SUPPLY.—The principal considerations in a water-
supply are—1st, the abundance of the source; and 2nd, the
purity of the water. To commence any works likely to fail in
quantity, would be the greatest misfortune which could be brought
upon a growing community, as the deficiency would tend to
injurious limitations at the very times when abundance would the
most be required; namely, during peculiarly hot or dry seasons.
In the second place, if the water is not pure and soft, it will be a
permanent source of disease and expense. Dr. Lyon Playfair
has calculated the consumption of soap necessary, in consequence

of an increase in hardness from 2° to 16°, to be equivalent to an annual expense of 4*s*. per head of the entire population, or four times the present charge in many towns of a full supply. The well-water of Ormskirk is excessively hard, as shown by the following analysis, contrasted with the water from the Bath spring :—

ANALYSIS.

Water from Wheatsheaf pump	.	.	80·0° of hardness.
Water from Bath spring*	.	.	5·9 ,,
Well in excess .	.	. .	74·1 ,,

This ˙74·1° of hardness in excess, will require 14 lbs. of soap extra with each 100 gallons, to wash with the same facility as with the Bath spring water ; 14 lbs. of soap, at 5*d*. per lb., is 5*s*. 10*d*.

The Bath spring is about one mile from the town ; it is one of several similar springs in the district of a like quality. The temperature, which is almost permanent throughout the year, shows that it rises from a deep source, and consequently will not be diminished or affected by local causes. A reservoir would require to be made, from which to pump the water for use ; the site is peculiarly favourable for this, and the necessary works may be cheaply carried out. I have not had the necessary time at my disposal to make out an estimate in detail, but there will be no difficulty in completing the works by private subscription, should the rate-payers decline to undertake them. It has been found, in similar works, that a dividend of 7 per cent. may be obtained, even should the first cost of the works reach 1*l*. per head of the entire population, which in Ormskirk would make the estimate upwards of 5000*l*., a sum by no means necessary ; the cost of pumps would however, as shown in another part of this Report, be 8725*l*.

The land in which the springs rise belongs to Edward Stanley, Esq.; the high ground on which a service reservoir would require to be made, to the Earl of Derby : and the probability is that Mr. Stanley and his Lordship will be disposed to treat liberally with the rate-payers should they undertake the works for the sole benefit of the town. The whole of the water-supply for Nottingham and Carlisle is pumped; the charge to cottages is 1*s*. 3*d*. per quarter, or rather more than 1*d*. per week; the supply in both these cases is in the hands of a private company, who work for a dividend.

RECOMMENDATIONS.—*Boundary for the purposes of the Act.*— I beg to propose that the boundary of the township be the boundary for the purposes of the Act.

---

* This sample of water was taken from the Bath Spring, November 27, 1849.
Temperature—Air, 49°.
Water, 51°.

Qualification and number of members to compose local Board.—The local Board to consist of nine members, to be elected as the Act directs: namely, that every person shall, at the time of his election as member of the said local Board, and so long as he shall continue in office by virtue of such election, be resident, as in the said Public Health Act, 1848, is required, and be seized and possessed of real or personal estate, or both, to the value or amount of not less than 500*l.*; or shall be so resident and rated to the relief of the poor of the township upon an annual value of not less than 15*l.*

Day of Election.—The first election to take place within one month after an order in council or provisional order shall have been obtained. The annual election to replace the retiring members to take place on the second Monday after the 25th day of March in each year.

First Returning Officer.—The chairman to the Board of Guardians, or, in case he should decline or from any cause be unable to serve, the deputy chairman to the Guardians, to be the first returning officer.

SUMMARY OF CONCLUSIONS AND RECOMMENDATIONS.—As the result of my examination of the town and township of Ormskirk, I beg respectfully to lay the following summary before your Honourable Board for consideration:—

1. That the town is not so healthy as it may be, on account of badly constructed houses and undrained streets, imperfect privy accommodation, crowded courts and lodging houses, large exposed middens, cesspools, and other nuisances; and that no adequate powers for effective local government at present exist.

2. That excess of disease has been distinctly traced to the undrained and crowded districts, to deficient ventilation, and to the absence of a full water supply, and of sewers and drains generally.

3. That the condition of the inhabitants would be improved, their comforts increased, and the rates reduced—

   i. By a perfect system of street, court, yard, and house drainage.

   ii. By a constant and cheap supply of pure water under pressure, laid on to every house and yard, to the entire superseding of all local wells and pumps, which are proved to be expensive.

   iii. By the substitution of water-closets or soil-pan apparatus for the more expensive and noxious privies and cesspools, some of which exist, and by a regular and systematic removal of all solid refuse at short intervals.

   iv. By properly paved courts and passages, and by a regular system of washing and cleansing all courts, passages, slaughter-houses, footpaths, and surface-channels, and by forming and maintaining good roads throughout the district.

4. That these improvements may be realized for the estimates given, and, if the works are managed with economy, they may be made not only self-supporting, but a source of income.

5. That the direct charges stated will be the means of a direct and indirect saving to the inhabitants generally, but to the labouring man especially, of many times the amount to be paid.

6. That the outlay will not be burthensome or oppressive to any class of the community, as the capital required may be raised by loan, and the interest upon it reduced to an annual or weekly rent-charge.

The Public Health Act is, therefore, not only necessary, but it will be of the greatest advantage to the rate-payers; and, with the exception of section 50, I beg respectfully to recommend that your Honourable Board will grant permission that it may be applied at the earliest period to the town and township.

I have the honour to be,

My Lords and Gentlemen,

Your obedient servant,

ROBERT RAWLINSON.

The General Board of Health,
    &c.   &c.   &c.